NM Kron £1

CU00968040

Trout Farming Manual

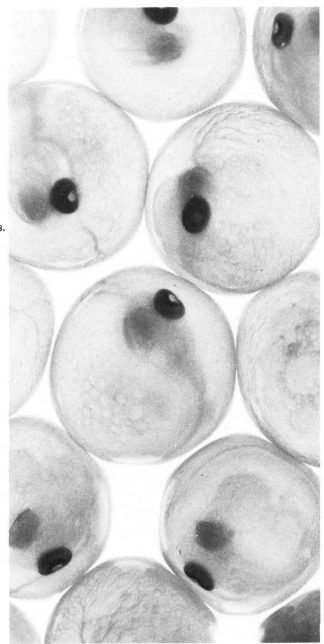

Frontispiece. Brown Trout
eggs, showing eyed embryos.

Trout Farming Manual

Dr John P Stevenson

Fishing News Books Limited
Farnham, Surrey, England

Stevenson, John P
Trout farming manual.
1. Trout
2. Fish-culture
I. Title
639'.375'5   SH167.T86
ISBN 0 85238 102 6

Type set by Traditional Typesetters Ltd.
Printed in Great Britain by Whitstable Litho

Contents

v

List of illustrations and tables

viii

Acknowledgements

The author wishes to express his thanks to the following:
Avington Trout Fisheries Ltd for figures 49, 62-70 and 74
CY Mouldings Ltd for figures 25, 52, 54 and 55
Grice and Young Ltd for figures 19, 33, 37, 51, 61, 80-82
M J Hancock for figure 83
Industrial Tank Specialists Ltd for figure 29
Irish Trout Industries Ltd for figures 2 and 56
Marcultura SA, Spain for figures 23, 24, 31, 34, 42-44, and
    47-48
Ministry for Conservation, Division of Fisheries and Wildlife,
    Victoria, Australia, for figures 20-22 and 30
Mixaerators Ltd and Dr Bass for figures 39-40
Roy Shaw for figures 71 and 73
Skretting A/S for figure 45
Test Valley Trout for figures 1, 8
Trafalgar Fisheries for figures 5-7, 9-10, 12, 14-15, 28,
    35-36 and 50
Mr L Peart for table 4

xi

Introduction

Fish farming, usually of carp, has been carried out for many centuries in many countries – in China, in ancient Egypt and during the great days of the Roman empire, in paddy fields and irrigation ditches, in lakes, in swamps and in the cloistered quiet of monastery ponds. But it is only in recent years that intensive and semi-intensive culture of the brown trout, *Salmo trutta*, and the rainbow trout, *Salmo gairdneri*, has become a widely accepted commercial venture, which, in the majority of those countries in which it is possible, is now becoming increasingly focused on the rainbow trout.

Rainbow trout are natives of the Sacramento River region, on the west coast of the United States of America, but have been successfully introduced into the waters of many other countries. Brown trout, a species highly variable in appearance, are natives of European waters though, like the rainbow, they are now widely distributed through many continents.

Zoologically, both species belong to the family Salmonidae, which forms a part of the order Isospondyli, a word meaning 'equal vertebrae'. All fish belonging to this group have the air bladder connected to the gullet by a pneumatic duct, and the pelvic fins are abdominal in position. The order contains a number of families, from which those with which we are here concerned may be distinguished by the presence of a small, fat 'adipose' fin on the hinder part of the back, between the dorsal fin and the tail. One of the differentiating features of brown trout is that the edge of the adipose fin is tipped with red.

In essence, commercial trout farming is not difficult, though like any other enterprise it has its pitfalls for the unwary. This book has been written as a practical guide for those without a great deal of experience, who may be considering the possibility of investing in a trout farm or hatchery, and for those interested in taking up work on a fish farm.

Information on certain aspects of fish farming techniques, for example stripping eggs from sexually mature hens, is not readily available elsewhere and therefore has been dealt with in some detail, but the major part of most chapters is calculated to convey general rather than particular ideas, and to offer some advice on desirable as well as undesirable practices and conditions.

In those chapters in which scientific matters have been mentioned, the layman has been in mind rather than the scientist so that, although precision may have been lost, hopefully it has been replaced by a text more easily under-stood by those unacquainted with scientific jargon. Where scientific terms have of necessity been used, they have been explained there and then, or listed in the glossary.

Diseases as such have not been dealt with at great length. Two useful books are recommended in the appendix, one written for the layman, the other for the specialist. However, it is the author's experience that the majority of fish farmers have neither the facilities nor the expertise to enable them to carry out the rigorous examinations and tests necessary for an accurate diagnosis of any other than common and easily recognizable conditions – and an inaccurate diagnosis can be worse than none at all.

Few diseases cause immediate large scale losses. Most start almost imperceptibly, building up slowly into what eventually becomes an obvious disease condition. If the fish behave in any way abnormally, flashing, gasping at the surface, congregating round water intakes; or if visual signs such as bloody patches, darkening of colour, protruding

2

eyeballs or other evidences of physiological disturbance are seen, first of all check that farming techniques are as they should be. A large proportion of diseases on fish farms are the direct or indirect result of poor husbandry. If everything on the farming side appears to be in order and if, on examination of affected fish, the cause of their condition is not immediately obvious, then is the time to call in a consultant.

However, it is useful from the point of view of farm hygiene and management to have some idea of what microbes are, what they do, and what the fish itself is capable of doing about them without human assistance. Chapter 9 has therefore been written in an attempt to provide a little elementary information on these topics, in the hope that it will enable the layman better to understand some of the sometimes rather incomprehensible recommendations made to him in connection with the control and prevention of diseases on his farm.

A great deal of valuable and detailed information on equipment, its installation and maintenance, is obtainable from manufacturers and their agents, whose advertisements can be found in fishery journals. If these are not available, recommendations or sources of information can often be obtained from government agencies concerned with fisheries or water control, or from consultants or veterinarians involved with fish diseases. Specific descriptions of equipment have therefore in most instances been omitted. However, an attempt has been made to indicate the type of installation that may be feasible for the site under consideration or, conversely, the type of location that may be suitable for a chosen installation.

Much the same comments apply to the paragraphs on nutrition – detailed information, feeding schedules and advice on diets are available from the manufacturers. Most fish farmers, like housewives, are in the position of having to feed their dependents on what is available on the local market. There is little point in listing minutiae such as the optimal amounts of an essential amino-acid or mineral in micrograms per gram of diet or per kilo of body weight, because the majority of farmers cannot in any case do much

3

about it since they are unlikely to have the experimental facilities necessary to enable them to make a critical analysis of the results. Nutritional requirements have, therefore, like equipment, been referred to only in general terms.

Nevertheless, it is worth remembering that both equipment and pelleted diets are marketed by commercial firms concerned with selling their own products. Consequently their recommendations, however excellent they may be in relation to the items they supply, may apply only to those items, and may specifically exclude those of their competitors. If there is any doubt about the quality of the water or the suitability of a site, equipment, diet or procedure, it is usually worthwhile to obtain independent expert advice. A suitable firm or individual can often be recommended by the editorial desk of fishery journals, or through the company with whom the premises and stock are to be insured. The fees demanded will be repaid several times over in the saving of wasted time and money, not to mention unnecessary worry.

Although pelleted food may not be available in all situations, the composition of wet diets has not been detailed because it varies widely from country to country depending on the availability of natural resources. Some details are given in books listed in the appendix.

While large farms are set up on a sound financial basis by experienced businessmen, smaller installations may be established by individuals or families, sometimes with one or two additional employees, as a means of providing a reasonably adequate income, which at the same time permits the owner and his family to live in surroundings of considerable natural beauty, away from the noise and tribulations of city or surburban life. Small farms can also provide, if not a living in themselves, a valuable income additional to that derived from a pension or other investments. However, even small concerns must be in a position to make a sufficient profit and, as has been mentioned elsewhere, it is usually not economical if the annual output falls much below 12 tonnes. Sufficient initial finance must therefore be available to set up a farm capable of producing at least this tonnage, and of carrying it through

4

the first two years of production. It is possible to establish a farm on a smaller basis, but if that is attempted there is a fair chance that it will fail to cover expenses.

There is no doubt that many people are attracted to fish farming or rod letting both as an interest and a life style, and if properly researched it can be rewarding from many points of view. Nevertheless, the market must be realistically assessed, and it should be emphasized that the work can be hard, cold and wet, though if the profits are sufficient to provide adequate food, warmth and shelter and a little pleasure, there is a lot to be said for being your own master.

While it is hoped that this book will provide some of the information necessary to be able to think constructively about setting up a fish farm, running it smoothly and turning it into a successful enterprise, it should be borne in mind that at least a whole volume could have been written about each of the chapter headings and even, in some cases, some of the paragraphs. Further reading is recommended in the appendix.

Finally, remember above all things that fish live in water; and water, if not a universal solvent, comes pretty close to it. If there is any chance of its picking up a contaminant you can expect it will do so, and the fish will be exposed to the consequences. An ample flow of good quality water from a pure source unlikely to be polluted is the first essential for any fish farm if it is to stand a chance of becoming and, more importantly, continuing as a successful commercial enterprise.

1 Water

It may seem to be stating the obvious to say that the first
essential for a trout farm is an abundant supply of good
quality water, but it is surprising how many people overlook
the importance of a comprehensive assessment of the flow
that will be the life blood of the farm.

Flow rate   Measurement of the flow rate on just one or two days is of
little use. Information covering maximal and minimal flows
over two or three years should be obtained, if possible, as
well as the minimum flow in drought conditions and the
maximum during heavy flooding. The situation is more
easily assessed if an existing farm is being bought, because
records should be available; they should be examined
carefully and checked. If a new farm is being developed
data may be more difficult to obtain. A local or state
authority with responsibility for the waters in the district
may be able to provide information, and it is useful to talk to
local people, particularly commercial fishermen, anglers and
farmers.

A reasonable idea of the rate of surface flow may be
obtained by measuring out a length of river (say 100
metres) and placing marks at each end of the measured
distance. A floater of some sort (a twig will do) is thrown in
above the start line, and the time it takes to get to the finish

taken with a stop watch. It must be emphasised that this will convey no information about differences in rates of flow at the banks or along the bottom.

The quantity of water passing through a farm is best measured by running the effluent over a flat surface of known dimensions, with vertical walls fitted with a depth gauge. A structure of this sort can be made in concrete or, if required only on a temporary basis, by placing a flat plate of some sort on the bed of the outflow and holding it in place with sandbags which are then built up to make a more or less vertical wall on either side of the flow. This arrangement results in the total flow running over an area of known dimensions. The width of the bottom is known, the depth of water can be measured, and the rate of flow (velocity) given by a suitably placed current meter. The total volume flowing in unit time can then be calculated or read off from hydraulic engineers' tables. These also give the volume of water emerging from a pipe of known dimensions if the velocity is known. Current meters can be borrowed, hired or bought from scientific instrument manufacturers.

In a properly planned installation there should be no danger of flooding, though if the farm is in an area of heavy seasonal rainfall special precautions may be necessary. The site should be selected with extra care and adequate by-passes constructed.

No farm should be established in a place where the water supply can fail. Even a periodical deficiency of water is undesirable. However, low flows can temporarily be offset by means of artificial aeration. Recycling water on a short term basis can help, but it entails recycling the accumulated detritus and microbes as well, and cannot be considered a useful method unless sophisticated filtration techniques are used. Even then, it cannot be recommended, as no commercially practicable filtration device will eliminate the smaller micro-organisms.

A number of authorities have calculated suitable flow rates for trout culture. It has been stated that 960-1440 m^3 per day is needed for production of one tonne of trout. While it is clear that an abundant flow is most desirable, these figures may be on the high side. Other sources quote 500-650 m³ per day per tonne production at 15°C. These calculations refer to intensive production; a somewhat lower flow rate is acceptable for semi-intensive methods such as those used for trout culture for re-stocking. However, average temperatures as well as fluctuations about the mean must be taken into consideration, since the amount of dissolved oxygen in the water depends on the temperature.

It is important to remember that the quantity of water available limits the number of ponds or other culture facilities, and therefore also places a limitation on the total output of the farm in terms of fish tonnage. If artificial aeration is used, the tonnage per unit volume of water can be doubled.

Quality   Although a good flow of water is a basic essential, the quality of the water is also important. A neutral or slightly alkaline pH is best, perhaps pH 7-8 is optimal. Acid waters having a pH much under 6·0 should be avoided.

pH can be measured with a fair degree of accuracy by means of pH papers, which are marketed by manufacturers of laboratory chemicals. The local pharmacist may be able to advise on a source. A paper is torn out and dipped in a sample of the water. The colour it assumes is then compared with a colour chart which forms the back of the book of papers, and the pH read off.

A more accurate assessment may be made using a comparator. Sets can be obtained from scientific instrument manufacturers or manufacturing chemists and are supplied with full instructions. Briefly, a drop of indicator (a chemical which changes colour at different pH values) is placed in a test tube and the colour compared with a set of standards supplied with the outfit. This type of outfit can also be bought for the purpose of measuring other chemical components of water – chlorine, for example.

For a high degree of accuracy a pH meter must be used. Electrodes are placed in a water sample and the pH read directly from the dial. Combined pH and oxygen meters are available, and some include temperature compensating

9

or measuring devices.

The mineral content of naturally occurring fresh water varies according to the terrain through which it has passed and the substances it has dissolved both from the rocks and the atmosphere. Hard water is that which contains large quantities of calcium carbonate and calcium bicarbonate. Other salts, such as those of magnesium, may also contribute to the hardness. Since bicarbonates buffer the water – that is, they tend to prevent large alterations in pH – the pH of hard water is more stable than that of soft water. This should be borne in mind if chemical treatment of fish farm water is undertaken, for instance for the purpose of eliminating a parasite. Total hardness is expressed as the equivalent amount of calcium carbonate present in parts per million (ppm) by weight. Frost and Brown (see appendix) state that there is a threshold hardness of about 150 ppm calcium carbonate above which trout thrive but below which they grow less well. The rate of growth, however, is not directly proportional to the hardness of the water. The acidity of water is due to a number of factors, among which is the CO_2 content and mineral acids. Biological oxygen demand (BOD) is one commonly used parameter of water quality. It is the quantity of dissolved oxygen, in mg/litre, required during stabilization of the decomposable organic matter in the water by aerobic biochemical action, and it provides an assessment of the quantity of organic matter present in the water. A good sample should not take up more than 20 mgm/litre of dissolved oxygen. Large quantities of organic matter in the water will, of course, tend to lower the oxygen content and so reduce its suitability for fish farming.

Trout eggs are susceptible to 0·1 mgm/litre of chlorine, and adult rainbows to 0·3 mgm/litre. Nitrates mostly derive from nitrogenous organic matter originating from animals, and the presence of nitrites, which will oxidize fairly quickly to nitrates, indicates recent organic pollution.

Water emerging from springs may have a high dissolved iron content, and if the iron should precipitate in the hatchery – which it can if oxidized naturally or by bacterial action – it may settle on the surface of eggs or the gills of fry, and smother them. A number of minerals can be toxic in certain concentrations, but assessment is difficult to make as it depends on a large number of other factors such as the pH of the water, the temperature and the presence of other ions. Rainbow trout alevins are susceptible to zinc concentrations of 0·04 ppm, so that alkaline water running through galvanized piping can pick up enough to cause losses in a hatchery.

In many parts of the world, where authorities have been established to control the quality of the potable water supply to more or less densely populated areas, thorough chemical analyses of the water may be available. If not, as is commonly the case in undeveloped or sparsely inhabited regions, the fish farmer should have analyses carried out, remembering that it is the water that enters the farm that matters, rather than that at the source. If chemical analyses are not easily available, water can be piped into a test tank with trout in it. The fish themselves are the best biological test.

Borehole water pumped straight into a hatchery may be supersaturated with nitrogen, which can be eliminated by aerating the water before use. Nitrogen supersaturation causes gas bubble disease.

Temperature and oxygen Spring or borehole water is particularly suitable for hatcheries and, although it may be a little on the cold side during the summer in temperate climates, it should also be used for brood stock, as it is not likely to be contaminated.

The temperature of emergent spring water in western Europe is usually fairly low, about 6°-10°C, though in warmer countries it may be 11°-15°C. Water arising from shallow springs varies considerably both in quantity and temperature, but that from deep springs will be more consistent in both respects.

Temperature fluctuations in water are important to the fish farmer. The preferential temperature for growing rainbow and brown trout is in the region of 15°C. Though rainbows will survive a transient 25°C it will do them no good, and 20°C is the maximum they are likely to survive in for any length of time. Brown trout are less tolerant.

Growth of both species more or less stops at 4°C. Optimal temperatures for hatcheries are rather lower than those for older fish: something in the region of 10°-12°C is best for eggs and fry to the swim up stage. In temperate climates the most important time of year for trout growth, which depends very largely on temperature, is from spring to autumn, when the temperature of the water flowing through the farm should not fall much below 10°C nor rise above 18°C. Mature fish spawn when the temperature drops, but may also be affected by the length of day. In the tropics, spawning may occur at any time of the year, though it is often correlated with a temperature drop.

Quite apart from its direct influence on the trout themselves, water temperature has a very important effect on its capacity to hold oxygen. Water containing as much oxygen it can hold is said to be fully saturated. As the temperature increases, the quantity of oxygen that can be dissolved in water decreases, so that while fully saturated water at 4°C contains 12·88 ppm dissolved oxygen, at 20°C it will contain only 9·00 ppm. Stated briefly, warm water holds less oxygen than cold water (*see Table 1*).

Both rainbow and brown trout require a minimum saturation level of 6 ppm, but to allow it to drop to that level is undesirable. They should always be held in fully saturated water.

The saturation level of water is also affected by altitude, less oxygen being present in the water at saturation level at high altitudes. As a rough guide, a drop of 0·5 ppm should be allowed for every 300 metres increase in altitude.

In temperate climates it is during the warm weather that the water flow is likely to be least. This is also the period when the fish are most active, taking more food and using more energy and, consequently, more oxygen. Additionally, oxygen is consumed by decaying organic matter so that waste food and excretory products in the water will make an additional contribution to an oxygen deficiency. Summer is also the time for proliferation of algae (algal blooms) and other water plants that produce oxygen during the day but absorb it at night when they are unable to photosynthesize. It is in conditions such as these that the oxygen content of

Table *1*. Oxygen content of fully saturated water at various temperatures.	Temperature (°C)	Oxygen solubility (ppm)
	0	14·32
	1	13·92
	2	13·57
	3	13·20
	4	12·88
	5	12·52
	6	12·21
	7	11.91
	8	11·62
	9	11·33
	10	11·10
	11	10·83
	12	10·61
	13	10·38
	14	10·15
	15	9·96
	16	9·76
	17	9·55
	18	9·35
	19	9·16
	20	9·00
	21	8·82
	22	8·67
	23	8·41
	24	8·36
	25	8·22

the water may fall to such a low level, particularly at night, that fish are asphyxiated. If at such times the water flow cannot be increased, artificial aeration must be used and the stocking density of the trout decreased.

2 Sites and installations

Sites Assuming a good supply of water of suitable quality, the course it pursues on its way to the farm should be carefully checked. The land adjacent to it on both sides should be studied, taking particular account of human activities such as agriculture, mining and forestry. Housing developments are highly undesirable.

Run-off and seepage from agricultural land can be contaminated with toxic chemicals such as insecticides and crop sprays. The sprays themselves can drift over the water when they are being applied, particularly if aircraft are used. Silage liquids contain organic matter which, on decay, consumes oxygen and depletes its concentration in the water.

Existing developments in the neighbourhood of the site can, of course, be seen, but future proposals should also be investigated if possible. The owners of land upstream should be known and their activities considered.

Freshwater sites should be as high up the water source as possible, so long as the flow is sufficient. Although it is not always feasible to own the land right back to the source, it is a clear advantage to do so. On the farm premises themselves, the land on both sides of the water should, where possible, be owned.

Another fish farm upstream can be damaging. It may not be well managed and, whether it is or not, it can at any time be affected by disease problems which can be, and usually are, disseminated downstream. In any case, accidents can happen, and a spillage of disinfectants such as iodophores or chlorine can have disastrous results. Careless discharge of water after scrubbing out tanks can sometimes be very nearly as damaging. Incidents of this sort should be recorded in detail as they may have consequences involving litigation.

Assuming there are no foreseeable sources of contamination, the natural configuration of the proposed site itself will, to a large extent, determine what can be done with it, and whether it is capable of being developed into the type of farm envisaged. Requirements for a tank installation for intensive production of portion sized fish for the table market (*Fig 1*) will obviously differ from those for the establishment of a Danish-type pond system (*Fig 2*) concerned with providing fish for re-stocking and these, in turn, will differ from those for a hatchery and brood stock ponds.

Fig 1. Fresh water site with circular tanks. Note demand feeders.

Fig 2. Danish-type earth ponds.

Water circulation Whatever the system to be developed, the most reliable and cheapest way to circulate water is by gravity. For this there must be a sufficient drop in ground level from intake to final outflow. If the initial intake is from a lake or river at a lower level than that on which the farm is to be sited, or if a hatchery and broodstock ponds are to be supplied from a borehole, pumping will be necessary. This adds to both capital and running costs.

If a pump is to be used, it must be duplicated in case of mechanical failure: it will in any case have to be taken out of service from time to time for maintenance. The duplicate should be powered by an alternative energy source so that it can be put into use in case of supply failure. One electric and one diesel powered pump are the safe minimum, and both must be capable of lifting the necessary quantity of water to the required level. If cost saving is very important, one pump capable of being driven by either of two motors should be installed, one of the motors being electric and the other diesel. Though this will provide a solution to failure of one of the motors, it will do nothing to remedy a break-

16

down of the pump itself.

Intensive cultivation of rainbow trout may be carried out in ponds, tanks or raceways. In order to avoid constant repetition of these three types of accommodation when general reference is made to them, they will in future be referred to as culture facilities or, for short, simply as facilities.

Danish-type mud ponds
A common type of culture facility is that developed in Denmark, in which a source of water feeds individual mud ponds arranged in parallel. In some cases there is a single line of ponds supplied by a feeder channel, each pond discharging into an effluent channel (*Fig 3*). It will usually be necessary to dam the river just above the farm in order to provide the necessary fall between the feeder channel and the ponds, and between the ponds and the effluent channel which may, in some cases, be the river itself or may discharge into the river further downstream.

Depending on the topography, it may be possible to install a double row of parallel ponds (*Fig 4*). In this case the feeder channel will have to be divided into two, each channel feeding its own row of ponds and each pond discharging into a back channel (*Fig 5*) which in turn flows through a screened outflow channel and so returns to the river (*Fig 6*).

The initial farm intake, which may be through one or more sluices, should be screened to prevent entry of detritus or undesirable fish such as predators, into the supply. Screens are commonly made of corrosion resistant metal or of plastic. They should have a suitable mesh size and be easily accessible for cleaning. Horizontal intake screens are preferable to vertical ones, which can become frequently clogged.

If the lie of the land permits, it is advisable to provide a by-pass channel above the top pond, to allow flood water to drain straight back into the river.

The supply channel is usually in the form of a stream, though if water is pumped up from a river, the initial supply will be piped. In either case, there is usually a piped supply into the pond, which may be screened (*Figs 7 and 8*)

17

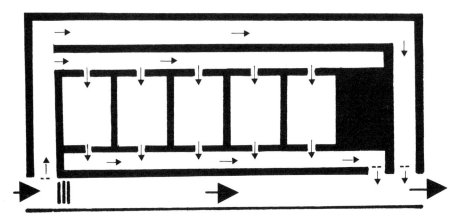

Fig 3. Diagram of Danish-type pond system. Single series of parallel ponds.

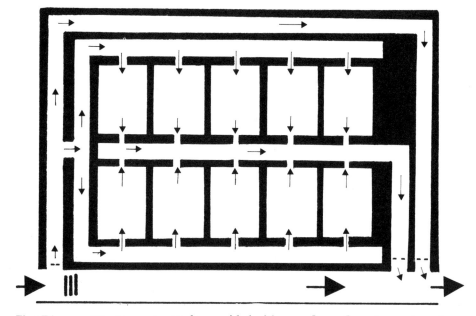

Fig 4. Diagram of Danish-type pond system. Double series of parallel ponds.

or may be provided with some form of aeration such as that shown in *Fig 9* in which a wheel constructed of four discs rotates in the water flow, causing it to splash. In some cases, however, the supply to each pond may be by way of a sluice, preferably screened.

18

Fig 5. Back channel
showing effluent discharge
from ponds.

Fig 6. Screened outflow
from back channel.

Earth ponds may be of any size, but they should be
manageable, and a rectangular shape of about 30 metres by
10 metres is common (*Fig 10*). There is nothing to prevent
it being larger or smaller, depending on the configuration of

19

Fig 7. Screened inflow to earth pond.

Fig 8. Screened inflow to circular tank.

Fig 9. Rotating paddle wheel on inflow pipe to aerate water.

Fig 10. Earth pond.

the land and the proposed lay-out of the farm. Irregularly shaped ponds may look pretty, but are impractical. A recommended depth is 1 metre at the intake, sloping to $1\frac{1}{2}$ or 2 metres at the outflow.

There is little point in going into too many details about pond construction: the advice of a consultant should be taken. However, that is not to say that the operator cannot do the job himself, particularly if he has had previous experience, and a few pointers may help.

If the dampened earth is sufficiently clayey to be screwed up into a ball in the hand and keep its shape, it will probably be sufficiently impervious to retain enough water. If not, it will be necessary to line the ponds with a plastic material. Obviously, this will increase the capital outlay. One of the advantages of Danish-type ponds is that they are not costly.

Butylene liners are expensive but good, and last a long time. Cheaper types of reinforced plastic are obtainable, though not necessarily in the required width. If it is necessary to overlap the sheets but at the same time obtain a waterproof joint, the easiest way to do it is shown in *Fig 11*. Dig a longitudinal trench about 25 cms deep along the line of join of the two sheets. Align the edges of two sheets and bed the aligned edges into the trench (A). Fill in with heavy earth (B). Now take the free edge of the upper

Fig 11. Diagram to show method of lining ponds with plastic sheets to obtain waterproof join
A: both sheets overlie each other at one side of pond.
B: trough being filled with earth to bed down the ends of the sheets.
C: top sheet is taken over to other side of pond.
D: completed operation.

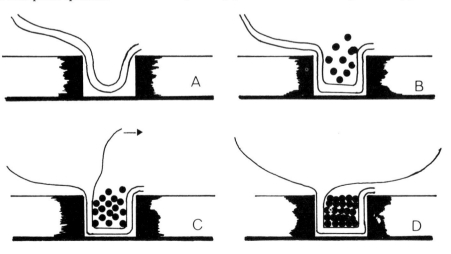

sheet and turn it over completely so that it lies on the far side of the trench to that on which the lower sheet is lying (C). The two sheets will thus lie alongside each other, joined by a more or less watertight seal (D), and will not move in relation to each other.

The perimeter banking of the pond should be sloped and the plastic sheeting taken over the top of the banks so that it can be well bedded down with earth, which should be turfed to keep it in place.

The outlet of this type of pond should be a monk set in the banking adjacent to the outflow channel or back channel. From the base of the monk a wide-bore pipe discharges into the channel (*Fig 12*). Older types of monk may be made of wood or brick, but they are more usually constructed of concrete, fibreglass or metal and are best provided with a double slider and a screen. This is the Herrguth-type monk (*Fig 13*). A corrosion resistant metal

Fig 12. Discharge from earth pond into back channel.

23

Fig 13. Diagram of Herrguth-type monk, sectional side view. A, B: are metal or wooden sliders moveable vertically in grooves in the concrete surround S. A: regulates depth of water in pond. B: is set above ground level to allow cold water and debris from the bottom of the pond to flow over A at water level, and subsequently out through a drain. C: screen.

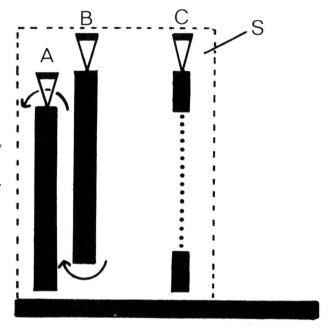

type is shown in *Fig 14* with the sliders and screen removed. These are shown in *Fig 15.* A single slider can be used but it will evacuate water only from the top of the pond, whereas the Herrguth-type evacuates the cooler and possibly dirtier water from the bottom. It can, of course, be set to evacuate the top water if required by removing slider B shown in *Fig 13*, or pushing it down to the bottom. A screen is necessary to prevent fish escaping. Sliders are usually housed in metal slides, but if more efficient prevention of leakage is necessary, neoprene slides are better.

More primitive and less dependable types of outlet can be installed by setting a wide bore outlet pipe at the water level required, screening the horizontally placed orifice with plastic mesh or galvanized wire. Other pipes can be set at different levels to permit alteration in the depth of water. They must also be screened and, if not in use, plugged. Small screens of the type described are liable to become clogged quickly, and they frequently come off the pipe, which itself can then become blocked. Monks are far better.

Fig 14. Metal monk installed at outflow end of earth pond with sliders and screen removed.

Fig 15. Screen and sliders for metal monk (*See Fig 14*).

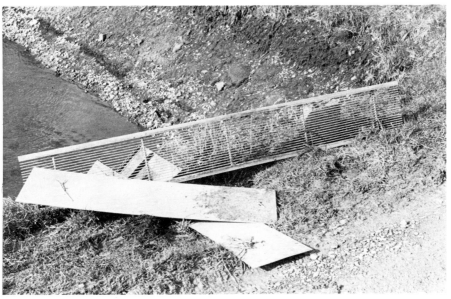

Tank culture Although an installation of the type described has many advantages, is cheap to establish and is entirely suitable for some types of culture, the majority of farmers use facilities constructed of concrete, fibreglass, metal or some similar hard substance that can easily be scrubbed down and disinfected. Some of the sectional metal tanks on the market can easily be erected or dismantled by a couple of men, and there is a wide choice of size, design and material. Information can be obtained from manufacturers, and many of the firms will be in a position to advise on the best lay-out for their products. However, it is prudent to get an independent opinion on the type of installation best suited to the project under consideration.

Circular tanks are popular because, as has been mentioned, they are easy to assemble and install, and the water supply and drainage can be arranged in such a way that a vortex is created which sweeps away much of the detritus, so that this type of facility is to some extent self-cleaning.

Corrugated, plastic-covered metal sections, curved to provide a tank diameter of suitable size, are frequently seen (*Fig 16*). They can be bolted together and sealed with a waterproof compound. The base is screeded in water-proof cement, with a fall to a central drain from which a wide-bore pipe discharges into the main effluent, which is often another pipe that collects the effluents from a row of tanks, and ultimately discharges into the river.

Fig 16. Corrugated metal fry tanks.

26

Fig 17. Circular tanks for growers. Note screened outflow and demand feeders.

The water level in the tank can be controlled by a vertical pipe which is a moveable fit into the main drain pipe, its height above the base of the tank thus being adjustable. The central outflow must be screened, usually by a vertical cylindrical plastic or metal mesh of sufficient height to project above the surface of the water (*Fig 17*). Screens of various mesh sizes are obtainable and the largest mesh size commensurate with the size of the fish should be used. The smaller the mesh the more rapidly it becomes choked. A screened overflow pipe of adequate dimensions should be fitted into the upper side wall of the tank.

The outflow pipe can be doubled to form a type of circular Herrguth monk, which can be effective in clearing small debris (*Fig 18*). A gap, the aperture of which must be set to the size of the fish to prevent their being swept out, is left at the bottom of the screen to allow detritus to be taken under it, and gaps must also be cut in the base of the outer pipe O, in order to provide a minimum of three legs on which it can stand so that its bottom orifice is above the base of the tank.

Tanks of this type can be dug into the ground as shown in *Figs 1 and 17*, or can be above ground level, depending

27

on the lie of the land in relation to the water supply. It should be noted that the tanks in *Fig 19* are covered with protective netting, and those in *Figs 20 and 21* are fitted counterbalanced metal screened covers in order to keep out predatory birds. The counterbalanced covers are shown better in *Fig 22*, in which the concrete counterbalance weights are seen to be attached one to each half of the screen, so that each heavy half screen can easily be raised to a vertical position to give access to the tank.

Figs 23 and 24 show surface facilities on fairly steeply sloping land. Here, the initial intake to the farm is sufficiently high above the final water discharge point to allow the supply to the tanks to be brought in by way of a concrete aquaduct, from which valved outlets are taken to each tank.

The outflow from larger circular tanks is directly through a central drain, though smaller-sized tanks are often provided with a moveable elbow pipe (*Figs 25 and 26*) which can be adjusted to provide whatever depth of water is required. The drain pipe must, of course, be suitably screened. Much the same system for controlling the water

Fig 18. Diagram of Herrguth-type central screened drain
S: screen
O: outer pipe cut away at base to permit discharge of bottom water
E: drain
The smaller figure on the left shows the cut away base of the outer pipe O.

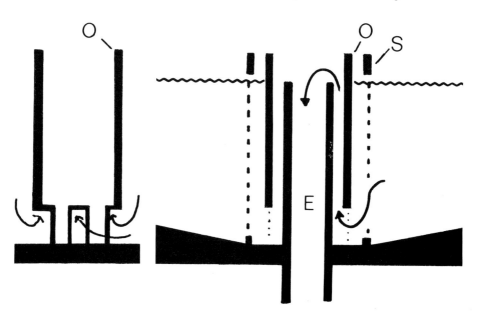

Fig 19. Installation of large circular tanks. Note netting for protection from birds.

Fig 20. Circular tank installation, with raceways in foreground.

Fig 21. Circular tanks. Note counterbalanced metal mesh screens for protection from birds.

Fig 22. Netting out fingerlings from circular tank. (Left)

depth is seen in some larger tank systems, such as that shown in *Fig 27*, where the installation is set on a concrete base. In this system the opening of the central drain from each tank is flush with the base and is covered with a flat screen which rests on nuts screwed on stainless steel or carbon fibre bolts let into the concrete, C. An upper series of nuts holds the screen in place, its height from the concrete being adjusted as necessary by screwing the lower series of nuts up or down. The central drain discharges through the valve shown at A, the valve B being closed. The depth of water is regulated by raising or lowering pipe P_1, which is a moveable fit in pipe P_2. Pipe P_1 discharges into the effluent pipe E, from which the water flows into the gulley D. If it is necessary, for instance, to grade the fish in

Fig 23. Fresh water site with circular tanks supplied from overhead aqueduct.

Fig 24. Higher up site shown in *Fig 23*. Note slope of land.

31

Fig 25. Fry tank.

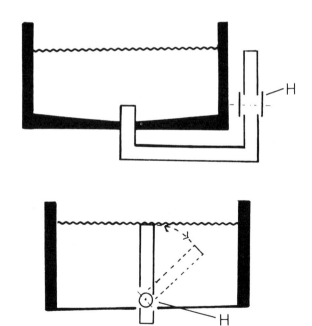

Fig 26. A common arrangement in small tanks and troughs to regulate depth of water. The drain pipe is hinged at H. (*See Fig 25*).

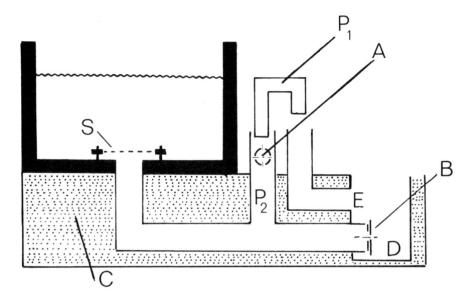

Fig 27. A more complex
version of *Fig 26* (See text)

the tank, valve A is closed, valve B opened and the water
level lowered until the screen retaining nuts are accessible.
Valve B is closed again and the screen removed. The pipe
terminating in valve B is constructed in such a way that
additional piping can be attached to it when required.
Thus, when valve B is opened again, the fish from the tank
are flushed straight out either into the gulley D or by way of
attached piping directly through a grader or into other
facilities further down the installation.

It is evident from what has been said that circular tanks
can provide a system of considerable flexibility which can be
adapted in one way or another to suit practically any
situation. The detailed design of installations of this type
depends on a number of factors among which are the lie of
the land, the requirements of the operator and the amount
of capital available.

Raceways Raceways are particularly suitable for large installations, but can also be used on a smaller scale (*Figs 28 and 29*). A double series of four raceways is shown in *Fig 30*, where each facility is 30 m long by 2·5 m wide, with a working depth of water of about 0·7 m. The water flow from upper raceways to lower is controlled by screened sluices. As many raceways as necessary can, of course, be placed alongside each other; larger installations may have a dozen or more.

Fig 28. Fry raceways.

34

Fig 29. Small raceways.
Note protective netting.

Fig 30. Raceways.

35

In many ways raceways are easier to manage and maintain than tanks, though in general the practice of discharging water through a series of raceways has little to recommend it from the hygiene point of view, as the lower water courses receive contaminated water from those higher up. However, so long as there are not too many raceways in a series and the water flow is sufficiently fast, there is little evidence to suggest there is very much to be faulted in the system, though a disease occurring in a higher raceway would probably be transmitted through the rest of the series.

Some very large raceway installations experience difficulty in obtaining a sufficiently massive supply of water, and consequently find it necessary to resort to re-circulation techniques, pumping the used water through filtration and aeration systems. However, there is no filter in practical, commercial use on a fish farm capable of removing viruses, and it is improbable that most filters have much effect on bacteria or other small organisms. Although toxic metabolites such as ammonia may be removed by biological filters, it is more than likely that some of these installations act as reservoirs of infection, re-circulating micro-organisms as well as water.

Nevertheless, a well designed raceway system has much to be said for it. It can be thought of as a modified type of Danish pond, with most of the advantages and few of the disadvantages. As with any other installation, those situated in countries susceptible to heavy seasonal rainfall should be provided with a by-pass of suitable dimensions, in order to obviate the possibility of flooding.

Raceways themselves are easily managed and cleaned, and access is good in a well-designed lay-out. Although the capital expenditure may be greater than in some other installations, the maintenance costs may be lower.

Effluent Used water from a fish farm sited on a fresh water source is inevitably discharged into a river, either directly from the facilities themselves or by way of a channel of some sort. Back channels in Danish-type farms may be used for over-wintering fish or for holding them prior to sale.

36

It is important that the flow from individual facilities should be immediately stopped in case of accidental spillage of damaging material. In some cases, such as the fry tank shown in *Fig 25*, there is usually no valve on the effluent pipe, but outflow of water can be stopped by turning the elbow pipe to a vertical position and cutting off the inflowing supply. Shutting off the supply is often the only way of stopping the outflow from most tanks, though valved installations of the type shown diagrammatically in *Fig 27* can immediately be isolated, while monks may be closed and the sluices in raceways can be shut down. In all cases the inflow must be stopped.

Filters   Although the initial water supply to the farm should be gated off to prevent entry of large debris, leaves and other such small bits and pieces can foul pipes and accumulate in the bottom of tanks. A leaf filter is useful. A simple design is shown in *Figs 31 and 32*. The water passes by way of a sluice into a chamber from which it flows beneath a grid, through which it rises and is subsequently discharged. The grid retains the leaves beneath it and a valved drain is set at the bottom of the filter so that accumulated detritus can be back-flushed when convenient. The grid itself must be made of heavy metal so that it is not lifted by the upsurging water, or it can be made in two parts, the lower being a mesh, the upper being a heavy plate with parallel rows of holes drilled in it, about $2\frac{1}{2}$ cms in diameter. The mesh is aligned

Fig 31. Leaf filter. Photograph taken from inlet sluice. Direction of main flow shown by arrow. (*See Fig 32*).

37

Fig 32. Diagram of leaf filter.
A: view from above.
B: plan of cross-section. Water flow is from intake (a) under grid (d) through which it wells up to flow out at (f). For cleaning, sluice (b$_1$) is raised to allow flow through by-pass (c). A second sluice is provided at (b$_2$) in case of flooding. Back flushing to get rid of accumulated debris is accomplished by opening valve (v) and allowing water and debris to flood out through drain (e).

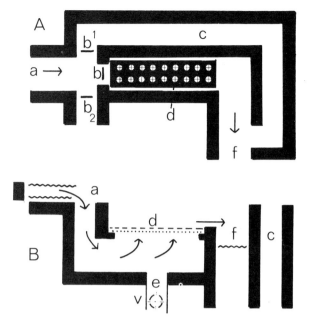

so that its cross pieces lie beneath the holes in the plate. Leaves are swept with the water below the grid and are held there. A by-pass with a sluice must be provided to allow for a continuous flow of water while the screen is being back-flushed or cleaned, or in case it becomes blocked.

Electricity   Electric installations for operation of pumps, security systems, lighting and other purposes should be designed and installed by electrical engineers: electricity and water do not mix, and unskilled work can be dangerous.

Access   The design of the farm must include adequate provision for easy access to all the facilities, not only for pedestrians but for trucks. If the site lends itself, a higher road for delivery vehicles and a lower road for loading is useful, so that fish can be flushed directly to or from transport, without handling.

Cage culture Trout can be grown on in cages floating in freshwater lakes. Investment costs are very much lower than those necessary for land-based installations. In some cases the cage may consist of nothing more than a net slung from a floating collar which can easily be assembled in the workshop from plastic piping and floats. In protected waters a method of this sort is satisfactory. However, there must be enough movement of water to provide a sufficient change for the fish, as they are trapped and cannot move from one area of the lake to another as they would if they were free in the same waters.

The mesh size of the net should be as large as possible, but commensurate with the size of the fish. Small meshes tend to become clogged with algae after a time, and prevent adequate water movement. Fouled nets should be taken out and dried in the dark, in a covered bin or some similar receptacle. The algae will dry off and can be removed.

Since artificial aeration will be difficult and water movement may not be great, the stocking density of trout in cages such as this will be low, and will vary in different lakes, depending principally on water movement and temperature at different seasons. On an experimental basis initial stocking with fry in the spring might be 10 kg/m^3 with a good water flow, using a small mesh. With experience of operating the site, the stocking density can probably be increased.

Installations of this type are attractive to poachers and can be difficult to protect. A residence should overlook the site, and a security firm should be consulted about the possibility of fitting battery operated sirens which activate if the top netting is disturbed.

Local fishermen can be helpful, particularly if they live in a house overlooking the farm or if they fish constantly in its vicinity.

Protection Apart from the obvious precautions of a high fence, locked gates and, perhaps, a couple of large dogs, many sophisticated protection devices are available. Those selected will depend on the type of installation as well as on

39

personal preference and available finance. One or two possibilities for the protection of floating cages have already been suggested. For land-based farms, the design of the alarm system should be such that it is not triggered by minor disturbances or by faults in the mechanism itself. Such occurrences will result, eventually, in no-one taking any notice of it. The advice of a competent security firm should be sought.

It is inadvisable to run a fish farm without insurance cover; too many unforseen and unforseeable catastrophes can occur. A number of insurance companies cater for the fish farmer and offer a wide spectrum of cover suitable for all types of installation.

One of the most common bases for a claim is that of pollution. If it occurs, the polluted ponds should be isolated if possible, recirculating and aerating the water if all the fish are not dead. The pollution source should be sought and notified, and water samples should be collected from above the pollution source, just below it, at the farm intake and downstream of the farm. Copious notes should be taken and photographs if possible. A witness should be present when the samples are taken. They should be carefully labelled with the place and date, and each should be divided into three: one for the person responsible for the pollution, one for analysis and one kept frozen in case of loss, or later enquiry.

Everything possible should be done to remedy the situation: the insurance company will be more responsive if prompt action has been taken. Insurers should be contacted as soon as possible and given the details they require at that time.

3 General farm practice

Stocks Farms without their own broodstock have to buy eggs, while those without a hatchery must obtain fry or older fish for growing on.

When purchases are made, they should be from a known, reputable source that can ensure delivery of high grade products from its own resources. If health certificates are offered these, too, should emanate from a reputable laboratory.

If at all possible, it is worthwhile visiting the farm from which the purchase is to be made. A competent farmer will be proud of his installation and his stock and will often be pleased to show them to a potentially good customer. On the other hand, some farmers are averse to clients visiting their premises, and this attitude does not necessarily imply they have something to conceal. Visitors may constitute a threat to the health of the farm: clothing, shoes, car tyres and hands could be contaminated with germs from the visitor's own premises. Many people have a habit, natural enough, of dipping their hands into the water of troughs or tanks. It is an undesirable trait which can convey an infection and is consequently irritating to a farmer who is concerned about the health of his stock and, at the same time, anxious to keep his customer's goodwill.

When re-stocking – and this applies to eggs as well as

fish – it is best to order half the required quantity from one supplier and the other half from another. One may fail to deliver, and some stock is better than none. A fairly common though unethical practice on the part of suppliers is to accept more orders than can be filled, and then deliver fish which ostensibly come from the supplier himself but which he has, in fact, bought in from other sources, thus leaving the purchaser with a mixed bag of fish from stocks that may or may not be good. It is worthwhile, therefore, when visiting the supplier's farm or hatchery, to assess its potential. To take a rather exaggerated example, if a hatchery advertises that it sells ten million eggs a year but, when visited, is seen to house half-a-dozen troughs capable of incubating at most about half a million eggs, it is reasonable to assume the owner is buying in eggs from other sources and selling them as his own. The same applies to fish: if the resources are not apparent it is logical to question where the supplies come from.

New deliveries should not be mixed with existing stock if at all possible, nor should deliveries from one source be mixed with those from another. They should be delivered into clean tanks and left there until it is certain they are in good health. One infected fish from a single source may be sufficient to infect the rest. Shipments should be carefully watched as they are unloaded and any signs of disease or anything by way of damage pointed out and noted. If complaints are made later, the supplier can always contend that the consignment was in good condition on delivery. Unloading new stock into already crowded facilities is asking for trouble. Nevertheless, if at some time after delivery the purchase exhibits a high mortality rate or shows other undesirable features which are not attributable to conditions on the farm, the matter should be taken up with the suppliers.

Hygiene   If diseases are to be avoided hygiene is important. In those farms in which a hatchery forms part of the installation, it should be treated as a separate entity, supplied with its own equipment and materials. Nets used on the general farm premises should not be used in the hatchery, and vice versa. Boots used on the farm should either be disinfected before they are taken into the hatchery by walking through a disinfectant bath, or they should be changed outside the hatchery for different boots. If there is any sign of fungussing or other disease on the farm, hands should be thoroughly washed, preferably in a mild disinfectant, before anything in the hatchery is touched. The same applies the other way round – when moving from hatchery to farm. There is little point in listing all the possibilities; it is largely a matter of common sense. Fry are subject to decimation by diseases such as infectious pancreatic necrosis which do no apparent harm to fish older than six months, although they can be infected with the virus but carry it without showing signs of the disease. In addition, adult fish can carry a certain amount of fungus which, if transferred to the hatchery, could do much damage.

Sick fish should be netted out and examined. If they are affected by parasites these can often be seen under quite low magnifications. They should be identified and treated accordingly (*see chapter 9*). The more common infections can sometimes be identified fairly easily and treated, but if there is any doubt a consultant should be called in.

Dead fish should be taken out of the water and if possible, the reason for death ascertained with appropriate steps being taken subsequently. A massive mortality occurring suddenly is usually due to contamination of the water supply with chemicals, though lack of oxygen is sometimes responsible. If small numbers of deaths are seen, numbers which gradually increase, building up day by day, the cause may be due to an infection. If at all possible, send living samples to a diagnostic laboratory by placing them in a plastic bag blown up with oxygen, despatching it by the quickest route. If that cannot be managed, take out of the water some of the fish that appear to be on the point of death, placing some in the deep freeze and others in the refrigerator at $4°C$, so that they can be made available for examination at a later date, which should be quite soon. If refrigeration is not available, make up a solution of saline, using two teaspoonfuls of salt to a litre of water. Then make up a formalin solution, using 90 parts of the saline solution just prepared, and adding 10 parts of formalin. The resulting liquid is known as 10 per cent formol-saline. If the fish are small, drop them in it as they are. If they are larger, slit them carefully open along their bellies. Send them to a laboratory for examination, either still in the solution or, if that is not possible, in a plastic bag.

If many diseased fish are taken out of the water, take samples and bury the rest, preferably in lime. Do not try to keep a 'hospital tank' – infected fish can be a source of infection for the others.

Scrub out and disinfect any tanks which have held infected stocks. As a general disinfectant for routine use chlorine is probably as good as any other. Obtainable as sodium hypochlorite, it is best bought in liquid form. 200 ppm in water will effectively disinfect equipment in an hour, though organic substances reduce its efficiency. It is toxic to fish and man and should be used with care. It can damage some materials, particularly metals. If it is used to disinfect fish tanks or other facilities, they must be thoroughly washed out with several changes of clean water before re-use. Chlorinated water discharged straight out of the farm will cause a great deal of damage to the environment. It must be carefully and heavily diluted. There may be local regulations governing the discharge of toxic effluents.

Weighing and grading Fish stocks are usually sold by weight. Each consignment should contain fish of a similar size, stocks must be graded from time to time. In any case, the feeding regime will depend to a large extent on the average weight of fish in the tank (*see Table 2, page 56*). Some farmers consider that fingerlings should be graded frequently because they grow at different rates, larger fish being able to get more food than those that are smaller, so starting a vicious circle resulting in a considerable size disparity. It is as well to judge the situation as it is seen: if there is an obvious difference in size, grade and re-distribute. Although cannibalism is not usually a problem unless the stock are underfed or exposed to too much light, there is no doubt that fry grow more quickly in the absence of competition.

44

On the other hand, frequent grading is likely to do more harm than good; some fish are always damaged, and whether they are or not, they do not feed for some time afterwards. It may be sufficient to grade once while the fish are in the fry tanks, once again on transfer to larger accommodation and thereafter two or three times while they are growing.

The way in which fish are graded depends to a large extent on the size and design of the installation. For a small scale operation they are usually crowded up to one end of the holding facility with nets and then netted out through a hand grader of the type shown in *Figs 33 and 34,* from which they can be distributed through plastic chutes into their new accommodation or, if that is not feasible, into plastic receptacles such as bins, in which they can be carried to their destination.

If a larger number of fish are being dealt with it is preferable to use a fish pump and adjustable grader

Fig 33. Hand grader.

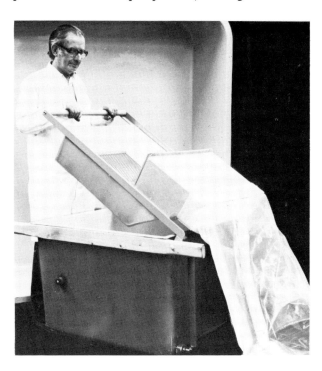

45

Fig 34. Hand grading.

(Fig 35). The fish are crowded in the tank or raceway or netted up to one end of the pond and then pumped through wide-bore hose into the grader, from which they are piped, according to size, for re-distribution. Some manufacturers supply a combined pump and grader which can be used as it stands or mounted on a truck or trailer and taken to the site

of operations. If the stock is held in raceways, a crowder with grading bars can be used. This is simply a screen with vertical bars, the width between which can be adjusted so that it functions as a grader. Usually it is mounted on a wheeled trolley which rolls along each side of the raceway, the crowder itself projecting down under the water to the bottom of the raceway. It is put in at one end and, if not motor driven, wheeled along to the other, pushing before it those fish too large to escape through the aperture between the bars, and leaving behind it the smaller stock.

Grading provides an opportunity to weigh and, if necessary, measure the fish. There are two measures in common use: total length and fork length. Fork length is the distance between the tip of the snout and the innermost part of the V of the tail. Total length is from snout to longest part of the tail when extended with the hand, all the fin rays being crowded together. Fork length is more commonly used, but if stock are bought or sold by length it is as well to make sure which method is agreed.

Fig 35. Automatic grader. Note raceways into which graded fish are piped.

Sale is usually by weight. Graded fish can be pumped straight into delivery tanks or trucks if they are fitted with a sight gauge (*see chapter 10*), but for redistribution on the farm or for sale of smaller quantities it may be more convenient to weigh them in a plastic bin on a beam balance. Place the bin on the balance, fill to the mark with water and note the weight (tare). Graded fish are hand counted into it and the weight again taken (gross). Tare weight subtracted from gross provides the net weight of the fish themselves. Their number being known, the average weight of each can be calculated (*see chapter 10*).

It is easier to weigh fingerlings in a bucket suspended from a spring balance. Do not use cheap plastic buckets – the handles are liable to come off. Spring balances are notoriously unreliable and should be checked from time to time against a beam balance which, so long as it is kept in good condition, will be a great deal more dependable.

Feeding and nutrition

Once in ponds or raceways, the stock must be carefully watched for signs of uneasiness or unusual behaviour indicative of trouble. Even if automatic feeders are used, the stock should be hand fed at least once a day, so that they may be properly observed.

Fish are cold-blooded animals whose body temperature is not controlled, but takes up the temperature of the surrounding water. Such animals are more susceptible to environmental changes, particularly temperature changes, than warm-blooded creatures who maintain a constant internal temperature irrespective of changes in the environment. The enzyme systems controlling the rate of reactions in the body of a fish function optimally at a specific temperature which, for trout, is in the region of 15°C. On either side of that temperature, the efficiency of the system falls off, so that at low temperatures the fish become slow and at temperatures which are too high the enzymes may be inactivated and cease to function, so that the fish dies.

During cold periods, therefore, fish will be lethargic and take only sufficient food to meet minimum requirements. At lower temperatures, about 5°C or less, a rise of ten degrees will more or less double the rate of metabolic activity, which decreases again above 17°-18°C. The rates of feeding thus depend to a large extent on the temperature of the water as well as the size of the fish and are given in charts supplied by food manufacturers. Both brown and rainbow trout feed best between 10°-15°C.

The rate of growth is also to a large extent dependent on temperature, and is best between the limits just stated. Length of daylight has an effect but it is small and, unless there is less than six hours light during the day, is best ignored for ordinary farming purposes. At low temperatures the internal activities will be insufficient for growth and food will be necessary only for continuation of normal body functions. As the temperature increases, greater quantities of food will be necessary to provide for energy, growth and maturation of the sexual organs and products. In young fish at optimal temperatures, the more food taken – within reason – the greater the rate of growth.

The diet of all animals must include fats, proteins and carbohydrates, as well as vitamins and small quantities of certain metals and minerals. Roughage is also necessary in order to provide bulk for the muscular movements of the intestine to work against so that the food is moved gradually backwards down the intestine, its various nutrient components being digested and absorbed as it goes. The indigestible remnants, packed closely together in the lower intestine, finally stimulate the muscles to eject them.

Rainbow and brown trout are carnivores, and need 40-50 per cent protein in their diet, though brood stocks coming up to spawning should have rather more. Suppliers usually provide special pellets for brood stock. Proteins are made up of chains of amino-acids. There are about twenty naturally occurring amino-acids, ten of which must be included in the diet of trout since they are unable to manufacture them from the break-down products of other amino-acids. These are known as the essential amino-acids and are: arginine, histidine, iso-leucine, leucine, lycine, methionine, phenylalanine, threonine, tryptophan and valine. So long as these ten are supplied in the diet, the trout itself can manufacture all the others from the protein in its diet. Protein is also used by trout for energy production, carbohydrates – which are essential for that purpose in many mammals – being necessary in the trout diet only at about a level of 8-10 per cent at most.

Fats are made up of chains of fatty acids. For good growth, trout must be provided with a particular type of fatty acid known as unsaturated. This is a chemical term which will not be discussed here, but unsaturated fatty acids are components of fats of low melting point; that is, they remain soft at low temperatures, some of them therefore being known as oils. Fatty acids belonging to the linolenic as well as the linoleic series are essential dietary components, as they cannot be made up by the trout from other fats. For normal growth, linolenic acid should constitute 1 per cent of the diet, as it is particularly important in this respect.

Fats serve various purposes in the body, an important one of which is as a food store to be drawn upon when necessary. They also provide body insulation and cushioning for some of the internal organs. However, if too much fat is provided it will infiltrate tissues, particularly those of the liver, and prevent normal functioning. Too much fat should not be given to sexually maturing hens as fatty deposits in the body make it difficult to feel the eggs when stripping.

Mineral deficiencies are not common, particularly in sea water, as most waters contain the majority of the substances required, though some pelleted foods contain mineral supplements such as calcium, potassium, magnesium, sodium, fluorine and iodine. In fact, very little is known of the mineral requirements of trout, and what is included in the diet is largely a matter of guesswork based on known requirements for mammals.

There is probably little synthesis of vitamins in the alimentary canal of trout, so that most must be present in the diet. All the known water-soluble vitamins are essential as well as vitamins A, E and K. Pelleted foods usually contain a sufficient amount of all the vitamins known to be necessary for birds and mammals and trout seem to do well on them.

The size of pellets suitable for fish of different weights,

50

together with feeding schedules, are obtainable from manufacturers. It is best to keep to them as far as possible, remembering that the amount of food given to a fish at any age will depend on its rate of metabolism, which depends largely on the temperature of the water.

As a market preference for pink coloured flesh exists in trout sold for the table, particularly in those over 1 kg in weight, special foods containing pigments such as canthaxanthin are available, and should be fed for three months prior to slaughter.

Other special diets are available, notably those containing anti-bacterial drugs for prevention or treatment of diseases such as vibriosis and furunculosis. They should be given on the first appearance of an outbreak because once the fish become sick they cease to feed well and consequently do not take the drug. Hence, those fish most in need of treatment will not get it. Nevertheless, delayed treatment is better than none, and may help to prevent an epidemic.

It is important to note that fish to which drugs have been administered must not be sold for three weeks after treatment has ceased.

The prime object of feeding is to supply an adequate amount of the correct nutrients at the least cost. Feeding efficiency is assessed by carrying out a calculation. The total weight of food given, in grams or kilograms, is divided by the gain in weight of the fish. For example:

$$\frac{\text{Gain in weight}}{\text{Weight of food}} = \frac{103}{150} = 1\cdot46$$

The figure 1·46 is known as the conversion rate (CR). It may sometimes be expressed as a ratio, 1 : 1·46, but is probably best left as the simpler figure – 1·46. It is clear that the greater the gain in weight of the fish, for a given quantity of food, the better the result. The more efficient the feeding regime, therefore, the lower the figure that will be obtained from the calculation. Thus, a conversion rate of 1·46 is better than a conversion rate of 2.

Fry should produce a better CR than older fish, and one-year-olds than two-year-olds. Swim-up fry may give a

CR of less than 1, which might be taken to mean that they are putting on more weight than the weight of food with which they have been provided. Obviously, this could not be the case and, in fact, the additional weight is due to uptake of water.

Some farmers claim a CR of about 1·15 for fish in tanks under optimal conditions, but a figure of 1·2-1·4 for growers is generally regarded as very satisfactory. Culture in earth ponds will probably reduce the feeding efficiency due to wastage of pellets, and a CR of about 2 or more can be obtained in good conditions.

As a means of assessing the condition of trout, a formula is sometimes used to provide a so-called condition factor. This is subject to so many variables, however, that it is of only doubtful value. However, it is set out here for those who might be interested in testing its usefulness. It is based on the premise that the weight of the trout is proportional to the cube of its length.

$$\text{Let } K = \text{condition} = \frac{100 \text{ x weight in grams}}{(\text{length in cms})^3} \text{ should} = 1$$

If K is less than 1, fish is in poor condition (long and thin).
If K equals 1, fish is in good condition.
If K is more than 1, fish is too fat.
(Trout are always fatter when sexually ripe, and in poor condition after spawning).

Measurements should not be made on individual fish, but averaged out from samples of twenty or more.

It has already been mentioned that some farmers prefer to hand feed on all occasions, while others install automatic feeders, a large diversity of types being available. Those chosen will depend to a large extent on the installation for which they are intended (*see Fig 36*). Demand feeders are useful for fish big enough to operate them (*Figs 37 and 38*). The hopper feeds into an aperture with a closing mechanism connected to a pendulum which projects down into the water. If a fish knocks the end of the pendulum, the aperture is opened, liberating a small quantity of food. It is surprising how quickly trout learn to operate the mechanism.

Fig 36. Hydraulically operated feeders.

It can, of course, be touched accidentally or operated unnecessarily and there is some waste, but on the whole the system is as good as most.

Other types of feeders are described in chapter 5. Similar types on a larger scale are available for installation on ponds, tanks and raceways, but for larger scale facilities mechanical blowers operated by compressed air are particularly useful. They scatter food over a considerable distance – for instance, down an appreciable part of the

53

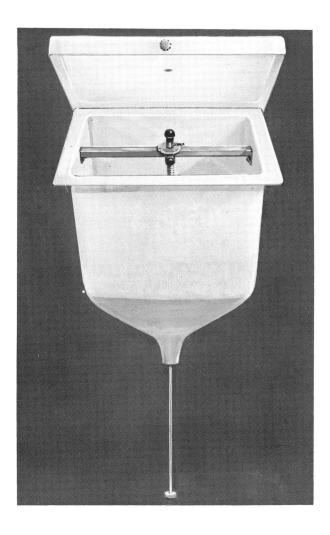

Fig 37. Demand feeder.

length of a raceway. Small models are available and larger ones can be mounted on a flat-bed truck or trailer and driven round the farm. One of the advantages of scattering the food widely – and this applies also to hand feeding – is that it gives the less aggressive fish a better chance.

Automatic feeders operated by electricity can be set to function at specified times. In general, the smaller the fish, the more often they should be fed, but overfeeding should

Fig 38. Filling the hopper
of a demand feeder.

be avoided because it soils the water and, moreover, is
expensive. Many farmers feed growers twice a day, in the
morning and towards evening, while others say that better
results are obtained if the fish are given a single meal each
evening. It is largely a matter of experience and opinion.

Where pelleted food is unobtainable, wet food has to be
supplied, and it is in any case cheaper to buy than
manufactured pellets in countries where waste marine fish
are readily available. However, the conversion rates
obtainable from wet foods are very much higher than those
from pelleted food, but labour is necessary for its
preparation. In addition, there is the danger of transmission
of disease-causing organisms in untreated food prepared
from wild fish whose state of health cannot be known. Data
on the composition and preparation of wet foods are given
in one or two of the books mentioned in the appendix.[1]

An approximate guide to feeding quantities is given in
Table 2 which sets out the weight of the ration per day in
terms of its percentage of the body weight of the fish.
Rate given is for water temperature of 10°C. Increase by

1. See, for instance, Edwards, Salmon and Trout Farming in Norway.

5-6% of the percentage for each 1°C rise in temperature up to 16°C.

Table 2. Feeding rates

No of fish/kg	5000	5000-650	650-250	250-100	100-50
Daily ration as percentage of weight of fish	5	4·5	3·6	2·8	2·2

No. of fish/kg	50-25	25-15	15-10	10-7	7-5	5-
Daily ration as percentage of weight of fish	2·0	1·7	1·5	1·4	1·3	1·2

Stocking density The density at which fish can be stocked depends largely on the oxygen content of the water, though to some extent on the experience of the staff and the amount of attention that is paid to the fish.

In good quality fresh water at 15°C, fully saturated with oxygen as it enters the tank, a commencing stocking density of growers can be tried at 25 kg/m³ with an optimal water exchange rate of 1·25 times per hour. With aeration, the density can reasonably be increased to 35 kg/m³ or more. However, very much higher stocking densities are maintained by many farmers, some of whom stock at about 60 kg/m³ or more with a water exchange of only 4-6 times per day with aeration.

Figures vary widely, and it should be remembered that the temperature of the water affects the amount of oxygen it holds; the higher the temperature the lower the oxygen content. One formula in common use indicates that at a stocking density of only 15 kg/m³ the total volume of water should be replaced every 1·5 hours.

Fig 39 shows the relationship between fish weighing from 10 gms-1 kg and the amount of oxygen they consume in terms of grams of oxygen used per ton of fish per hour. It will be seen that the oxygen requirements of smaller fish are very considerably higher than those of larger, so that the density at which small fish can safely be stocked is lower than that at which the larger ones may be held. *Fig 40* indicates the throughput of saturated water (*ie* water saturated with oxygen) in cubic metres per hour plotted against the tonnage of fish of mean weight 50 gms and 200 gms, at various temperatures. Here, it will be noted that the weight of fish supported at any one water throughput falls off as the temperature increases.

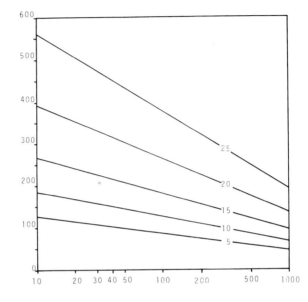

Fig 39. The oxygen consumption of rainbow trout between 10 gms and 1 kg at temperatures between 5°C and 25°C. Horizontal scale is logarithmic.

Fig 40. Saturated fresh-water requirements of rainbow trout between 5°C and 25°C at mean weight 50 gms (broken line) and 200 gms (solid line). Horizontal scale is logarithmic.

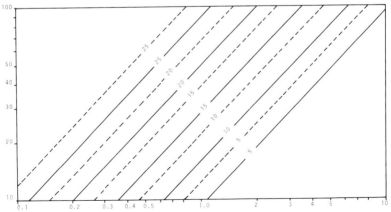

The lower the throughput of water, the lower the number of fish that can be supported. However, adequate aeration, capable of keeping the water saturated, will double the holding capacity in terms of kilograms of fish per cubic metre. If, for instance, the water throughflow will naturally support a density of 25 kg/m^3, good aeration facilities will increase the capacity to 50 kg/m^3.

Once more, some farmers assert that a high degree of aeration enables them to support five times the density of fish that could normally be maintained using only naturally aerated water, but these figures should be regarded with caution, as should those quoted previously, giving a stocking density of 60 kg/m^3 with a water replacement of only 4-6 times per day.

The higher the stocking density and the lower the water throughput, the greater is the exposure of the fish to toxic products of metabolism, such as ammonia. Stresses incurred by exposure of this sort render the trout increasingly susceptible to diseases and, once an infectious disease starts, it will spread through a crowded population with very much greater rapidity than it will through one in which each fish is reasonably comfortable.

Month old fry should not be stocked at a density greater than 15 kg/m^3 at most; 10 kg/m^3 is probably safer, at any rate for those with limited experience.

Weeds Weeds can be a source of trouble in the ponds of freshwater farms, and may also foul the nets of cages floating in freshwater lakes. Most farmers prefer to put up with them until the fish have been moved, when the vegetation can be raked out and hauled on to the bank. More thorough cleaning can be carried out when the pond is drained. Chemical treatment of weeds is not recommended as some of the products are to some extent toxic to fish.

Aeration The reason for aerating water is to increase its oxygen content and at the same time inactivate some of the more toxic products of the metabolism of the fish.

There are two very simple methods of increasing the oxygen content of a piped water supply falling into ponds or tanks: the first is to fit a flat board (a splashboard) immediately under the flow from the pipe, so that instead of falling straight into the tank the water splashes on the board from which it enters the tank in thin sheets and droplets. The second is to fit a plastic mesh round the orifice of the inlet pipe so that the water sprays through the mesh. Both methods can be combined.

Additional aeration may be necessary in conditions of low water flow or high temperatures; more particularly when both occur at the same time. Its effect on stocking densities has already been mentioned. Numerous types of aerators are available from manufacturers; it depends very much on the size and layout of the farm which kind is selected. The majority are electrically operated, and many are very efficient. Some farmers install a central air compressor from which piping is taken round the perimeters of the ponds, hoses being led from valved outlets at convenient points (*Fig 41*).

Water supplied to circular fry tanks, from radial arms with apertures along their length through which the water emerges, is generally sufficiently oxygenated, and that falling from an upper into a lower raceway may be taken down a cascade consisting of several steps, or may fall on a splashboard.

Fig 41. Aeration system operated from central compressor.

4 Marine culture

Both rainbow and brown trout can be adapted to a marine
environment in which they can be farmed until the
approach of sexual maturity. At this time salt water
becomes damaging to them and they therefore have to be
sold or moved to fresh or brackish water sites of low
salinity. Consequently, brood stocks cannot be maintained
on marine farms. Brackish water has advantages over fresh,
in that its saline content assists in the prevention of fungal
infections. From egg to a minimum size of 35 gms, young
fish must be cultured in hatcheries supplied with pure
fresh water.

While marine farming of rainbow trout is common,
brown trout are not farmed in this way because there is no
demand for them for the table, in competition with salmon:
and if cultured in salt water they are obviously unsuitable
for re-stocking fresh waters.

There is little doubt that so far as general husbandry
routines are concerned, it is simpler to farm in fresh water.
But it must be of good quality, and there must be a plentiful
supply at the right temperature, and there are a number of
circumstances in which marine culture has to be seriously
considered.

First, not all climates are suitable for fresh water culture
at all times. In northern Scandinavia, for instance, where

many of the techniques of marine trout farming have been developed, winters are long and cold, and fresh water temperatures are sufficiently high to promote good growth rates only for a few months in the summer. Yearlings do not, therefore, reach portion size in the autumn, so that sale of this product cannot be sustained in the face of competition from countries with warmer climates. Fish coming up to portion size after 18 months are necessarily expensive to produce. While the situation varies from country to country, and may be affected by import duties, transport costs and similar expenses, in general it is likely that the market for portion sized fish will be met principally by producers able to sell yearlings.

In such cases – that is, in cold countries with a suitable seaboard – marine culture may present an acceptable alternative and provide for a different market. Sea temperatures do not fluctuate as widely as those of fresh waters and so long as winter sea temperatures are not too low it may be possible, as it is in Norway, to maintain growth through the winter months, exporting $2\frac{1}{2}$ year old fish for 'family' consumption and for the hotel and catering trades.

Although circumstances are different, much the same principles apply to warm, arid regions with a good seaboard but a limited supply of fresh water. So long as there is sufficient fresh water of good quality to support hatchery and broodstock, trout can be grown in floating cages in the sea. In any case, fingerlings can be imported. Some Middle East states provide examples.

Secondly, the initial cost of setting-up a marine unit is considerably less than that involved in establishing a fresh water unit producing the same tonnage of fish. Major expenses are those connected with labour, net inspection and maintenance, grading and feeding, and the cost of the food and the stock itself.

Sea water The sea presents a more uniform environment than fresh water. For reasons that are not clear, it also seems to be a more aseptic medium than fresh water; one possibility is that its immense volume dilutes the concentration of pathogenic micro-organisms emanating from infected sources.

Full strength sea water has a total salt content of 34 parts per thousand (ppt) which exerts a buffering effect tending to prevent changes in pH. The salt also inhibits development of fungal spores and, consequently, of fungal infections.

The temperature at which sea water freezes is − 2·2°C, while fresh water freezes at 0°C. The saturated dissolved oxygen content of salt water, however, is in the region of 25 per cent less than that of fresh water at the same temperature, so that stocking densities on marine farms are much lower than those in fresh water installations. In warm sea water the dissolved oxygen content may fall to unacceptably low levels.

Site selection

A reasonably well sheltered site is essential, (*Figs 42 and 43*) though there must be sufficient water movement to ensure adequate re-oxygenation. Mere movement backwards and forwards of the same parcel of water through the moorings is not enough: there must be good mixing and circulation within the parcel itself to permit oxygen saturation at all

Fig 42. Floating cages in marine site.

Fig 43. Boats attending floating cages.

times. Wave motion is, of course, different from that produced by tidal flows and currents, but all three have to be taken into consideration.

The flow runs fastest during spring tides (*ie* immediately after full and new moon) and at that time, too, tidal waters reach their highest and lowest depths. There must always be a sufficient depth of water under cages at low water springs to provide a good clearance between the bottom of the cage and the sea bed.

It is when the tide is running fast against the wind that the most violent wave movements occur, though storms and surges will affect the situation and may be a dominant factor in some cases. Consequently, the vulnerability of the site to weather conditions is of prime importance, and also affects the design of the cages to be used.

On the whole, pollution in many countries is not likely to present such a problem as it does in fresh water sites in the vicinity of urbanized areas, though coastal industrial developments are clearly undesirable in most cases.

However, they are not necessarily always disadvantageous: nuclear power stations, for instance, discharge heated water which can increase the water temperature in their vicinity by a degree or two. Nevertheless, the possibility of pollution by accidental discharge of poisonous substances has to be borne in mind in connection with any industrial plant. In some cases, legislation may afford some protection to inshore fishery interests.

Fresh water emerging from rivers in the vicinity of the site will affect both the temperature and the salinity of the water and may contain contaminants, particularly if there are development areas situated further up the river. Run-off from coastal fields, particularly if farming is carried out, may bring with it contaminants such as crop sprays and insecticides, many of which are highly toxic to fish.

The sea bottom also needs consideration. A rocky bottom may provide clear water but at the same time present mooring problems, while fine sand can be disturbed by swirling water currents and taken up as a suspension that can damage the gills.

Government and local regulations may assist or hinder fish farming projects. It is important to bear legal requirements in mind and ensure that, where necessary, they are complied with. In some cases there may be objections from conservationists and those involved with water sports.

Once a feasible site has been selected, to which there are no legal, environmental or technical objections, the best advice that can be given is to take an option to purchase or rent, and set up a test cage. If that proves satisfactory in itself, representative samples of trout should be stocked and given a run for a season, careful records being kept of everything that occurs. After an objective assessment of the results, if all appears to have gone well the site will probably prove satisfactory.

Cage design Although submersible cages exist and are used commercially in Japan, and rigid-walled cages using galvanized or copper-based metal meshes have been constructed, the majority of marine fish farming is carried out in cages consisting basically of a floating collar with a flexible mesh

Fig 44. Floating cages. Note method of linking with shackles.

net suspended beneath it. On-shore tank installations using pumped sea water are not generally economical for routine growing-on purposes, and have been largely abandoned so far as trout culture is concerned.

The design of floating cages must depend very largely on conditions prevailing on the selected site: a cage design suitable for one location may be useless in another. In calm, protected waters, light structures consisting of nothing much more than three or four loosely linked floats can be used, while in more exposed situations the rigid framework of the net support must be of robust construction, able to withstand strong currents and heavy wave movements. (*Fig 44*). In this type of structure, each net is secured at its corners and at intervals along its edges to a rectilinear frame of either welded tubular steel or glass fibre reinforced plastic construction. Glass fibre frames are durable and require less maintenance than steel, which is subject to the very considerable corrosive effects of salt water, consequently needing regular and expensive maintenance and repainting.

Information concerning sea conditions such as wave, tidal and current effects on the site may be obtainable from universities, naval authorities or local meteorological stations. While it is essential that the cage support structure should withstand the worst the weather is able to do to it, over-compensation for possible adverse conditions can lead to unnecessary expense both in installation and maintenance costs. Fish farmers considering the possibility of setting up a marine installation are strongly advised to consult either manufacturers of sea cages or marine engineering consultants with experience in cage design. It is important that recommendations should refer specifically to the site proposed, and should not be made on a general basis.

Light cages – floating collars with suspended nets – may be moored in groups offshore and attended for routine purposes from small boats, but it is usually better to provide a moored floating walkway to which such cages can be attached, being additionally provided with their own moorings if current movements necessitate a more stable

Fig 45. Floating cages with automatic feeders.

anchorage (*Fig 45*). Where possible, it is preferable to moor cages of this type to a jetty with direct access to a quay: an arrangement that facilitates the work and reduces labour costs.

Stronger cages suitable for rougher waters are generally provided with one or more walkways as a matter of course, though it may be possible to attend them from a wide-beamed, stable barge.

Since trout jump out of the water, stanchions about 2/3-1 metre in height are generally fitted to the framework, and are either separately netted or function as top supports for the main net. They also serve as safety rails for personnel using the walkways and, additionally, can be used to support a top covering net which should be fitted to protect the stock against predatory birds. These top nets must be held taut and not allowed to droop below the water surface as, in those circumstances, the fish can become entangled and damaged and thus rendered more susceptible to disease.

66

However protected the position, attending to floating cages by leaning over the side of a boat is dangerous, particularly if the worker is alone and wearing heavy clothing. Walkways are safer, although they increase the installation costs.

Mooring blocks are usually made of concrete with heavy galvanized bolts let in. The blocks should be heavy enough to prevent shift of the cage. A cruciform shape holds better than the more usual cubic block. Cages should be attached to the moorings by chain or, for lighter structures, by nylon warp which should be protected by metal eyes in positions in which it is subject to chafe.

Nets and fouling Nets are made from a variety of materials; very frequently nylon. Again, specialist manufacturers' advice should be taken. The mesh must of course be commensurate with the size of the fish, a larger mesh being used for bigger fish. In all cases the largest possible mesh size should be used. The smaller the mesh the greater the degree of fouling and the lower the volume of water flowing through the net, the greater the resistance to water flow and the greater, consequently, the drag. Fouling, which can be extensive and rapid in some waters, increases not only the drag but the total weight of the structure and can sometimes be sufficient to sink the cage. The possible effects of fouling are matters for very serious consideration, affecting not only the design of the whole floating structure, but both initial and working costs in terms of materials, labour and time.

Nets can be treated with various substances to reduce the extent of fouling, and manufacturers should be consulted about methods and materials recommended for their products. No known treatment will eliminate fouling; the best that can be done is to reduce it. The extent of fouling, as well as the type, depends on the organisms present in the water and is much worse in some situations than in others. The type of fouling may also depend on the season.

As a general rule, nets are not likely to remain in good condition for longer than two to three years, depending on the degree of fouling and other factors such as exposure to the damaging effects of sunlight. They should be removed

67

for cleaning and maintenance when the fish are harvested, or when they are being graded, a procedure that should be carried out when size disparities become obvious.

Cage size   Choice of cage size depends to some extent on the site and to a rather larger extent on economic factors and management problems. A few larger cages are cheaper to buy and install than a number of smaller ones. On the other hand, the larger the supporting structure the greater the distorting forces to which it is subjected; and the larger the net enclosure the more difficult it is to handle and to service. It is usually inadvisable to install a cage with an underwater net volume of more than 1,000 m³. The preferred size in many cases lies between 200 m³ and 500 m³ for cages situated in tidal sites, though the volume of nets supported by light structures in protected waters may be less. It must be re-emphasized that both size and construction of netting and supporting framework depend entirely on conditions obtaining on the site itself, as well as on management requirements concerning initial outlay and labour and maintenance considerations.

Stocking densities   It has already been mentioned that the saturated oxygen content of sea water is considerably lower than that of fresh. Stocking densities in marine farms are thus appreciably lower than those in fresh water establishments. There is, however, less accumulation of detritus and often a greater throughflow of water, so that there is no accumulation of toxic substances. Some operators state that they stock at a density of 40 kg/m³, but figures as high as this should perhaps be treated with caution. A more realistic figure for a high grade product would be at most 25 kg/m³ and in many cases 10-15 kg/m³ would be sufficient. These densities apply to adult fish: fingerlings should be stocked proportionately less densely according to their size, as their oxygen consumption is greater.

Acclimatization   When approaching sexual maturity, both male and female trout are adversely affected if kept in sea water. Brood stock are therefore maintained in fresh water, as are eggs and young fry.

At 60-80 gms fingerlings can be transferred directly from fresh to salt water, though they will go off their feed for days or even weeks, and there will be mortalities as a result of both thermal and osmotic shock. Thermal shock – that is, shock resulting from an abrupt change of environmental temperature – can be reduced to some extent by gradual equalization of the temperature of the water in the delivery tank with that in the sea by lowering the water level in the tank and topping up with sea water, repeating the operation two or three times at intervals of between 15 and 30 minutes, until the temperature in the tank is more or less equivalent to that in the sea. This relatively rapid change of water will do nothing to reduce osmotic shock, which is due to the physiological upset resulting from an abrupt change from an environment in which fresh water has to be continually excreted and salt conserved, to one in which salt has to be excreted and water conserved (*chapter 8*).

If possible, it is preferable to acclimatize fingerlings to marine conditions prior to transfer into floating cages. Acclimatization should be carried out slowly over a period of at least a week and preferably several weeks. It can commence when fry have reached a weight of 40 gms or a little less.

If acclimatization facilities are to be incorporated in the farm, it must be planned and sited in such a way that appropriate mixtures of fresh and salt water can be provided, and this usually means that the site must be on the coast, or nearby, but accessible to a fresh water supply, which can be piped from a river.

Sea water is pumped in as required. Continuous flows of fresh and salt water are delivered to acclimatization tanks, the two flows being adjusted either manually or auto-matically to provide a salinity which at first must be low, gradually increasing throughout the duration of the operation to give a final salinity equal to or only a little less than that of the full strength sea water into which the fry will eventually be transferred.

If for one reason or another it is impracticable to provide a continuous flow of water of gradually increasing salinity, another system, considerably cheaper, is to install a mixing tank. This is an ordinary tank of a size similar to that of the acclimatization tanks used on the site. The inside wall of the mixing tank is marked with levels to which salt and fresh water must be raised to provide water of a given salinity (*Fig 46*). Each marked level denotes a different salinity in parts per thousand. If, for example, water at a salinity of 15 ppt were required, salt water would be run in until the 15 mark was reached, the flow stopped, and the tank filled up to the top mark (T, in the diagram) with fresh water. The marked levels can be calculated as a function of the known dimensions of the tank, or can be set by trial and error,

Fig 46. Salinity marking inside of acclimatization tank.

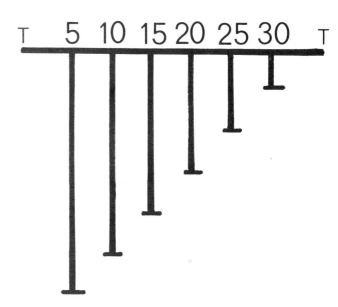

UPPER RIM OF TANK

T   5 10 15 20 25 30   T

BASE

70

measuring the salinity with a salinometer. They need not be too precise. It is useful to stagger the marks and paint vertical bars above each, so that if the mark is obscured, perhaps by running in a little too much water, its approximate position can still be seen.

Water of the required salinity is then run from mixing tank to acclimatization tank (*Fig 47*) where it is re-circulated and continuously and massively aerated. The fish are held in the re-circulated water for a period not exceeding 48 hours, when the water must be changed. At this change, water of increased salinity may be run in from the mixing tank. *Fig 48* shows an acclimatization tank being scrubbed out during a water change. It is essential that very thorough aeration be continued while the fish are held in re-circulated water.

Fig 47. Acclimatization tanks.

Fig 48. Scrubbing out an acclimatization tank.

Diet Where a plentiful and cheap supply of wet fish or fish waste is available, some farmers prefer to use a wet feed on economic grounds. The composition of such diets is well set out in Edwards' book[1] (see appendix) which should be consulted if wet feeds are considered. Although purchase of the various wet food components themselves is cheaper than the cost of good grade pelleted food, a great deal of labour is involved in preparation of made-up diets, so that total costs are likely to be more or less equivalent. There is an increasing tendency to use pelleted foods in countries where they are produced, or whose legislation does not prohibit their import.

Special pelleted sea water diets are available from manufacturers, who produce suitably sized pellets for both salmon and trout of all weights. Trout may do better on a salmon diet, which is higher in protein content and calorific value, though more expensive than that specifically manufactured for trout.

It has been said by one or two farmers that incorporation of 5-10 per cent salt in pellets fed to fingerlings for a few weeks prior to transfer to sea water assists adaptation to a marine environment, and it is also claimed that osmo-regulation is helped if pellets are damped – just sufficiently to feel damp to the touch – before being given to fish in marine cages. However, addition of water to pellets can reduce the vitamin C content and so result in spinal deformities.

Diets with an increased water content, such as Oregon moist pellets or a similar type, may usefully be fed as soon as the fry begin to take food after transfer.

Automatic feeders are frequently used, but can be wasteful particularly in floating cages where any food not taken immediately is dispersed. Fish as well as cages need regular inspection, and it is worth while keeping an eye on the type of wild fish in the vicinity of the cage. Hand feeding during these periods of observation and inspection is convenient, and is practiced by the majority of operators.

1. Edwards, Salmon and Trout Farming in Norway.

Protection Apart from design faults, weather damage, fouling or inadequate maintenance, one of the main problems for floating net cages is damage by flotsam. Debris of all sorts can be brought down on the tide, but unless it consists of exceptionally heavy objects such as tree trunks swept along by a swift current it is unlikely to do much harm to robust metal structures. However, semi-submerged objects such as rotten tree branches and pieces of wreckage can tear the nets, and if the holes are not noticed and repaired immediately extensive losses of stock can result. Predatory fish attempting to attack those in the nets can also cause damage.

While secondary nets slung outside the cage netting will assist, they increase the installation and maintenance costs and add to the blocking, drag and weight effects of accumulated fouling. Floating booms, sometimes with old netting slung beneath them may help, but tend to hinder routine operations by restricting access to the cages. Moreover, if large pieces of debris get inside such protective booms, they can be continually carried up and down through the installation by successive tides, causing more damage than would otherwise have been the case.

A warning device offers one possible solution. If an insulated wire is wound up and down, outside the cage netting, in a consecutive V-formation on hooks fixed to the upper and lower bars of the metal support structure, it will be broken if the netting is broken. The wire is connected to a nickel cadmium battery housed in a glassfibre case on the walkway, and so arranged that if broken it will activate a sound or light alarm, or both, which will be heard or seen at night by shore personnel. Fish in a net cage tend to swim round and round in the centre of the cage, and do not immediately migrate through a tear but, rather, filter slowly out as time goes on. As a consequence, if an alarm is actuated there should be time for a diver to place a temporary panel on the tear before heavy losses of stock occur. Such an arrangement is not unduly expensive, is simple to maintain and replace. Its cost may in any case be to some extent offset by reduced insurance premiums.

It has already been mentioned in connection with fresh

water floating cages that they present a temptation to vandals and poachers, particularly at week-ends and during the dark hours. Alarms of the sort described will assist in protection against this type of hazard. However, cage installations should always be overlooked by a residence. Large farms, if not permanently attended by at least one fishery employee, may require a guard on duty at night, week-ends and holidays. However, local commercial fishermen working locally and passing the cages regularly can be extremely helpful, particularly if their families live in a situation that overlooks the site. It is well worth while encouraging them to assist in protective activities by offering them the use of refrigerated or other storage facilities, or by allowing them fishing rights in waters over which the farm has exclusive rights.

5 Hatchery installation

While some fish farms are self-sufficient, producing eggs
from their own broodstock, raising the fry and growing
them on, others specialize in the sale of eggs, fry and
fingerlings. In both cases, establishment of a hatchery and
broodstock ponds is necessary.

Although many hatcheries are sited on rivers, a spring or
borehole source of water is preferable from every point of
view. Even in countries in which damaging diseases have
not been seen or in which the water supply emanates from
and runs through undeveloped areas where the chance of
contamination is small, there remains a degree of risk.
River water can be polluted in many ways at any time,
particularly in areas in which there is a degree of
urbanization.

It is recommended that the water source itself should be
within the boundaries of the farm. If that cannot be
managed, the run of water from source to intake should
preferably be under the absolute control of the farmer.

Accommodation One of the cheapest types of housing for a hatchery is a
covering of plastic supported on frames. Structures such as
this can be purchased ready for erection or may be home
made. Since light is damaging to eggs and young fish,
opaque plastic sheeting which will occlude all but a minimal

75

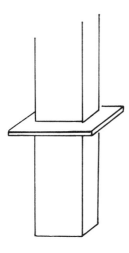

Fig 49. Diagram of flanged leg.

amount of light should be used. Accommodation of this type is best considered only as a low-cost initial investment to get the unit on its feet, or as a cheap, temporary extension to existing facilities. A more substantial building is a better long term prospect. Wood is relatively cheap in some countries, though susceptible to attack by insects. Galvanized iron sheeting or plastic coated metal on wooden frames can be used, though buildings of this sort get very hot in hot climates and very cold in cold countries. Double skinning with plastic sheeting can provide a degree of insulation or an inner wall of wood or other suitable material can be attached to the framework. In the tropics, cavity walling of this type can become infested, and internal panels should be easily removable for fumigation.

Pre-fabricated sectional concrete buildings are popular where they are readily available, but cement or other artificial building blocks are widely used. They have the advantage of lending themselves to the construction of durable buildings planned and designed according to the requirements of the installation, and can provide structures of whatever shape or size is necessary.

While adequate ventilation is essential, windows should be provided with some means of occluding the light, since it is damaging to eggs and young fry. All doors and windows should be fly proofed in warm climates, and doors and other openings must be large enough to permit easy passage of large equipment.

The hatchery building itself, or one adjacent to it, should provide accommodation for sorting, weighing and counting eggs and fry. It may be convenient, too, to add another room for cold storage.

Food is expensive and perishable and should be stored in dry, well ventilated conditions out of the way of rodents and insects – often not an easy matter. It is possible, with luck, to stop rats getting at food by placing sacks in ventilated cupboards on self-standing racks supported on stilts with flanged legs (*Fig 49*). Insects present even greater problems. Greasing the legs may nelp, particularly if a 'knock-down' insecticide is incorporated into the grease, but few preventive measures seem to affect the more determined species, particularly those that can fly. Insecticides, and insecticidal sprays in particular, should be used with caution in the vicinity of a hatchery, but some of the electric insect killers are useful.

On large installations food is often kept in hoppers (*Fig 50*).

As well as a store, office accommodation can be incorporated in the hatchery building and, where possible, it is also convenient to include staff toilet facilities and a locker room. However, if the farm is small and a residence of some sort is on the property or nearby – as it should be, for the sake of security – facilities of this sort will probably be in the house.

A garage or cover should be provided for vehicles, trailers and other mechanical equipment such as pumps and generators. It is important to include alarm systems, not only for security but to monitor the electric supply, water depth where overflows are possible, main and ancillary water supplies and any other equipment that could fail and

Fig 50. Food hoppers.

thereby endanger the stocks. Both audible and visible systems are advisable and the alarms themselves should operate both in the hatchery and the residence.

Troughs The classical hatchery is provided with troughs into which water flows from a feeder channel. This system has a number of advantages: it is easily kept under observation, the eggs and alevins can be seen at a glance, the whole process of development readily monitored, and there is little to go wrong.

The troughs themselves are usually made of plastic or fibreglass, sometimes of concrete or aluminium and occasionally of wood. Although it is possible to build home made troughs on the farm as a money saving operation, it is preferable to buy factory made equipment from a supplier, who will often be able to offer advice about the construction of the whole installation. Nevertheless, as is the case with suppliers of tanks, it is as well to remember that though their advice will be worthwhile in relation to the goods they supply, it will refer specifically to their own products, and probably exclude those of competitors. It is advisable to obtain impartial advice on all equipment.

An average sized trough will be $3 \cdot 0 \text{ m} \times 0 \cdot 5 \text{ m} \times 0 \cdot 25 \text{ m}$, though sizes vary. It will preferably be screened at the inflow to prevent entry of small pieces of detritus, and will necessarily be screened at the outflow to prevent alevins and fry being flushed out. Beyond the outflow screen there will be one or two overflow pipes. These may be vertically adjustable for height, to regulate the depth of water in the trough, or their orifices may be placed at the highest safe point to act as overflows, the water depth being regulated by an adjustable elbow pipe (*Fig 51*).

Egg baskets are made to fit the troughs. The mesh aperture is an elongated rectangle or oval of such a size that it retains the spherical eggs but allows the thin alevins to fall through to the water beneath (*Fig 52*). It is necessary for water to be forced upward through the mesh in order to provide adequate aeration for the eggs. In some cases the baskets are designed with a downward projecting baffle on their downstream end, which forces the water backwards

78

Fig 51. Outflow end of hatchery trough. Note: egg basket with angled mesh to induce upward flow of water; screen; doubled overflow pipes; elbow pipe to regulate water depth.

Fig 52. Egg basket and trough.

and upwards through the mesh (*Fig 53*), though some manufacturers design the mesh in such a way that the edges of the mesh apertures themselves are angled upwards, so that the need for a baffle is eliminated.

79

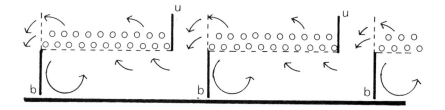

Incubators If space is limited or large scale egg production is envisaged, battery incubators may be necessary. These, again, are available from a number of suppliers. They consist essentially of vertically stacked plastic drawers, each drawer corresponding to a small trough and containing an egg basket and a cover (*Fig 54*). They are so designed that each drawer (tray) can be pulled out for inspection or attention. A common arrangement is for the water flow to pass downwards through each vertical tray stack, filtering through each one from top to bottom. Systems vary: some manufacturers prefer an upward flow of water, and there may be an individual flow to each tray. One of the advantages of incubators is that installations can be equipped with re-circulation systems in which the water can be heated or cooled and thus regulate the rate of development of the eggs. Although re-circulation is, in general, undesirable on a fish farm, it is not necessarily so dangerous in egg production as, apart from gaseous exchange, there is no excretion of wastes. However, adequate re-oxygenation of the water is necessary.

Large scale egg incubation can also be carried out in bottles (*Fig 55*) which may be made of glass, fibreglass or plastic. The water flow is upwards, through the bottom of the bottle, which is fitted with a filter or screen. The eggs are bathed in a continuously rising flow of water which escapes from the top of the bottle either through a screened pipe or, more straightforwardly, overflows over the top of the bottle which, in this case, is fitted with a perforated lid.

Fig 53. Diagram of water through egg baskets without angled mesh. Note that the solid upstream end of the baskets (u) deflects the flow downwards and the baffles (b) deflect it upwards through the eggs. Baskets with angled mesh do not require baffles. (Left).

Fig 54. Vertical flow incubator fittings.

Although vertical incubators have been developed primarily for egg production, alevins will hatch out satisfactorily in the system, though as soon as they begin to swim up they must be transferred to troughs or some similar small scale facility (*Fig 56*) where they can continue their development. Eggs should be kept in bottles only until they are ready to hatch.

Water distribution The water supply to the hatchery will, unless it is pumped from a borehole, almost certainly bring with it leaves, twigs and other small debris. A leaf filter, situated a little way upstream of the hatchery intake, is useful. An efficient type is described in chapter 2, but a subsidiary filter or screen is

81

Fig 55. Incubator bottles.

Fig 56. Fry troughs
(raceways).

useful immediately before the intake itself, and the main distribution channel to the troughs should be screened. It is essential to avoid accumulation of debris in battery or bottle systems.

The main water supply may flow directly into the hatchery, though the rate of flow must be adequately controlled. This will be easier if the initial intake passes into a header tank, but the layout will to some extent depend on the configuration of the land and on its slope, as well as on whether pumping is used. Whatever the layout, flooding must be avoided. The object is to obtain a constant, easily controlled flow that will provide the maximum volume of water necessary.

If bottles are used at an accessible level, their water supply must come from an inflow situated fairly near the ground; the same applies to upward-flow incubators. Troughs require a mid-level supply and downward-flow incubators must receive their water from above. All supplies, whether to trough, bottles or incubators – or, for that matter, to any other holding facility on a fish farm – should have an adequate by-pass so that the flow can be diverted when necessary.

Troughs can be supplied by way of a pipe with valved outlets, but an open channel is often favoured as it is more easily accessible for cleaning and inspection. The outlets may be in the form of adjustable elbow pipes which can easily be turned upwards so that their orifices are above the level of the water in the channel, thus cutting off the supply to the trough. Pushing them down again restores the flow, though this system can leak, and valves are often preferred (*Fig 57*).

The necessary water flow through troughs and incubators will depend on their size and design. Details will be supplied by the manufacturers but, in general, the flow through an average sized trough should be 5,000 litres per day for each 10,000 eggs, which is the average number for one basket. Five baskets in a trough require a water flow of 20 m^3/day at 10°C, or 40 m^3/day for a pair of troughs. However, the flow should, with experience, be regulated by eye to provide a sufficient run through the troughs to lift it into the baskets at a sufficient rate to allow it to well gently up through the mesh and so support the eggs without too much movement. The available water supply should be adequate to at least double these quantities, for safety.

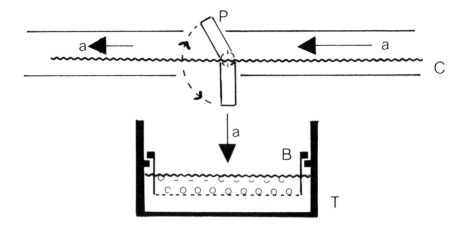

Fig 57. Diagram showing arrangement of adjustable elbow pipe in feeder channel (c) to troughs. The elbow pipe (p) is easily pushed up or down to stop or start water flow into the troughs (t) (b) is the egg basket and the arrows (a) indicate direction of flow.

Eggs consume increasing amounts of oxygen as they develop and, if the temperature should increase, the oxygen content will fall.

For a 16-tray incubator the average flow will probably be about 45 m³/day, though precise figures for various temperatures will be recommended by the manufacturers. The necessary through-flow depends to a large extent on the design of the apparatus and on its capacity.

When the eggs begin to eye, the water flow should be increased, and increased again when hatching starts.

Layout The manner in which the troughs themselves are arranged depends on the design of the building and the space available. There are two very common layouts. The first is for the supply channel to run along one wall of the building, providing a supply to paired troughs aligned at right angles to the wall, their outflows falling into an open effluent channel or a pipe leading to the main effluent (*Fig 58*). The second plan, perhaps more common, is to have a supply channel running centrally down the length of the hatchery, with paired troughs on either side of it (*Fig 59*). Troughs are sometimes placed in series down the length of the room, like a set of miniature raceways, each series being provided with water from a single valve (*Fig 60*). This arrangement is preferred if the water supply is limited.

84

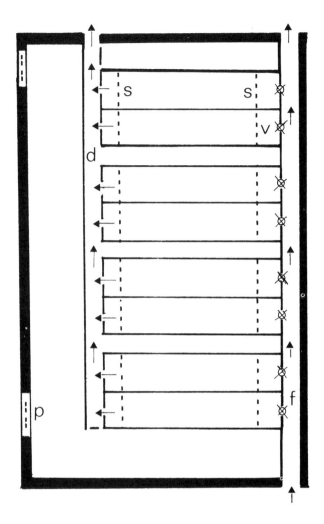

Fig 58. Diagram of hatchery with single series of troughs in parallel.
D: drain.
F: feeder channel.
S: screen.
V: valve.
P: door to building.
Arrows indicate direction of water flow.

In some hatcheries half the space is devoted to fry tanks such as those shown in *Figs 25 and 61*, while in others these are placed outside under cover. They must be protected from the sun and the weather.

There are innumerable possible variations in the layout, and it is important that subsequent development of the installation should not take place in a haphazard way. Alterations should be minimal, and carefully planned.

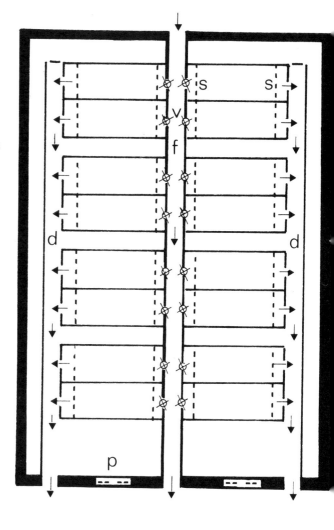

Fig 59. Diagram of hatchery with double series of troughs in parallel
D: drain
F: feeder channel (central, supplying both series of troughs).
S: screen.
V: valve.
P: door to building.
Arrows indicate direction of water flow.

Random additions and re-arrangements may seem useful at the time, but can end up as an inefficient and possibly dangerous mess of leaking hoses and pipework festooned with loops of electric wire, with fish of all shapes and sizes in differently shaped tanks in inaccessible places. Such an arrangement may be tolerable (usually it is not) in an experimental set-up, but it is no use to the commercial fish

Fig 60. Diagram of
hatchery with linked
troughs.
D : drain.
F : feeder channel.
S : screen.
V : valve.
P : door to building.

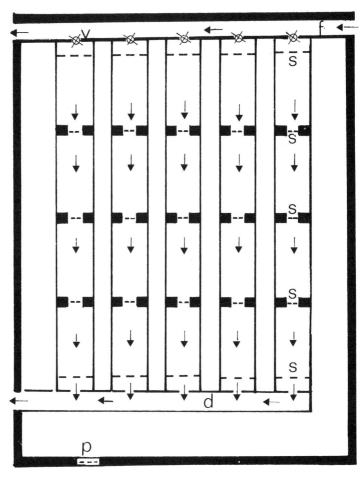

farmer who is trying to make a profit. If, at first, it is not
possible to provide all the equipment and facilities that are
desirable, proper, planned provision should be made for
later additions. If the initial design turns out to be
unsatisfactory, or if a later decision is taken to install a
different system, strip the whole thing down in the off-
season and re-design it completely.

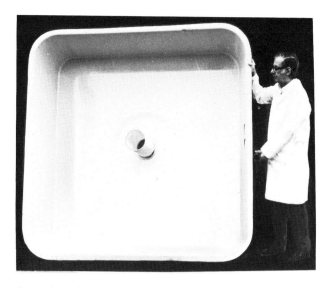

Fig 61. Fry tank. The central outlet will be screened and orifices are seen on the right for provision of inlet or overflow piping.

Automatic feeders A number of manufacturers produce automatic feeders. Some are operated electrically, some hydraulically and some by compressed air. They consist essentially of a hopper to hold the food, which falls by gravity into a distributing device. It is clear, therefore, that the food must remain dry, or it will jam. In most cases the food in the hopper itself will be dry; it is that in the outlet that gets wet either by splashing or condensation, and it is important that the design chosen should not be one that regurgitates wet chunks of consolidated food that fall straight to the bottom of the trough.

Hydraulically operated designs work on the waterwheel principal. A small quantity of inflowing water is diverted through an adjustable aperture to fall on the vanes of a wheel whose speed of rotation depends on the size of the aperture. The wheel is geared to a worm which forces out food pellets falling on it from the hopper (*see Fig 36*). In other cases the hopper discharges on a rotating horizontal disc which, as it rotates, passes under a fixed arm which sweeps the food off it, into the water. Similar designs are operated electrically, and other electric feeders can be made to release measured amounts of food from time to time, or be provided with timing devices which ensure ejection of

88

food pellets at pre-set intervals. These are probably the most useful types, since they can be regulated to provide feeds of known quantity at set intervals during the day, automatically shutting down at night.

6 Broodstock and stripping

Broodstock ponds Broodstock are usually held in raceways or larger artificial ponds provided with the same pure water used for the hatchery. Sometimes they are held in circular tanks, but should not be crowded in any way. It is advisable to keep them in concrete or other hard facilities that can easily be cleaned and disinfected (*Fig 62*). In warm climates the water flow should be sufficient to keep the temperature under 18°C, and the pond depth should allow the fish to escape from direct sunlight, though it must not be so deep as to be unmanageable. Some form of shade is desirable. Poles about three metres in height may be placed at suitable intervals, opposite each other on opposite sides of the pond, with cords stretched between them to keep off birds. The cords should be decorated with bunting or strips of foil that will move in the wind. The water flow should be more than adequate, and aerators should be on hand in case of oxygen deficiency. A central aerating system is better (*Fig 41*).

The stocking density should be low and the fish should at all times be well fed (*Fig 63*), more particularly for the six months prior to spawning. Special diets are obtainable from food manufacturers. However, overfeeding should be avoided, as should a fatty diet, as it appears to affect development of the eggs and too much fat in the tissues makes stripping more difficult.

Fig 62. Brood stock ponds.

Fig 63. Feeding mature broodstock.

Broodstock Females can sometimes be stripped at two years, depending on the conditions under which they have been reared, though the eggs are not as good as those taken at three years old, when broodstock are more usually stripped. Stripped hens may be replaced in the ponds and subsequently used in their fourth and fifth years, though there may be a falling off in the egg yield and the size of the fish at these times makes them difficult to handle. The aim should be to establish an annually maturing stock, ready for stripping each season at three years' old. Afterwards, they may be sold or, if a put-and-take fishery is run, transferred to that. Males can be stripped on several occasions, at intervals of perhaps three or four days, though there is no point in keeping them for longer than one season.

If the stock is held in raceways or similar narrow installations, crowding racks can be used to gather the fish together for selection, but if larger ponds are used it is convenient to net them out into small floating cages – one for cocks and the other for hens – from which they can easily be taken out with a hand net for stripping (*Fig 64*). Whichever method is used, the fish will be crowded and some form of aeration should be used. Water can be sprayed over them from a hosepipe temporarily fixed in position to effect a certain degree of aeration. The brood stock will have to be fed and nurtured for three years. They are valuable fish and should not be exposed to risks. If they are lost, it will take a year to replace them, and the eggs will also have been lost.

Although the technicalities of genetics are best left to geneticists, a competent stockman will ensure that the eggs he grows on from his own broodstock will come from two types of female: first, those that have matured early and are ready for an early stripping; and second, those that mature later, so that a longer stripping season results. In this way, with careful selection over a number of years, egg production can be spread over several months. In addition, the largest and best fish producing the highest yield of good-sized eggs should be selected, and appearance and colour should also be taken into consideration.

Fig 64. Netting fish out of temporary net cages into which they have been placed ready for stripping.

Anaesthetization prior to stripping

Some hatcherymen prefer to anaesthetize the fish during stripping on the grounds that it makes them easier to handle and is therefore less likely to damage the fish. If an anaesthetic is used, the trout must be netted out in twos and threes and placed in the anaesthetic bath prior to stripping, being returned to the water immediately afterwards to recover.

Tricaine methane sulphonate (MS222) is the most commonly used anaesthetic. It is soluble in water and should be used at a concentration of between 15 and 300 ppm. It tends to stiffen the muscles and thus makes stripping more difficult.

Carbon dioxide bubbled through a porous stone is sometimes used. The precise amount cannot be predicted since it depends to some extent on water temperature, but as soon as the fish ceases to respond to stimulus, treatment should cease.

Another alternative is chlorbutanol. Dissolved in a few ml of 70 per cent alcohol, it should be added to the tank to give a final concentration of 8-10 ppm. Benzocaine can also be used. It is dissolved in a few ml of acetone and added to the water to give a final concentration of 25 ppm.

Stripping arrangements

Arrangements for stripping depend on a number of factors, not least of which is the climate. Hot sunshine may necessitate the use of a temporary shelter, particularly for the eggs, which can be very quickly damaged by exposure to direct sunlight and hot temperatures. In cold climates exposure to very cold water can numb the hands, as well as other parts, of the workers, and it may be necessary to build a stripping house over the end of raceways, or provide some other type of shelter which can be moved about the site.

The mechanics of getting cock and hen fish separated and conveniently to hand depends on the arrangement of the facilities, the techniques employed, the number of fish and the number of workers. The essential features of the operation are that the fish, male or female, should be on hand for the stripper at the right time. It is usual for one worker to strip the hens and another the cocks. Stripping

Fig 65. Floating cages for replacement of fish after stripping. Note that the cage is divided into two compartments, one for cocks and the other for hens.

hens is tiring, and one worker should be able to relieve another. The strippers must also be provided with the bowls into which the eggs and milt are to be expelled. Fish should be returned to the water – usually into another couple of floating nets – immediately they have been dealt with (*Fig 65*).

Trout are usually stripped into plastic containers which must not be contaminated with any trace of disinfectant or detergent or, for that matter, anything else. A bucket of clean hatchery water should be to hand, together with a ladle of some sort, in order to top up with water each bowl as it is filled with eggs.

Stripping There are two principal methods of stripping: the dry and the wet. Perhaps the majority of workers prefer the wet method, in which a quantity of water is placed in the bowl. The eggs are stripped into it and the water prevents the damage that might be caused to them if they were discharged against the hard surface of the bowl. Milt from a male must immediately be added since contact with the water initiates swelling of the eggs, thus closing the

94

micropyle (*chapter 7*). However, this does not happen instantaneously, and a competent stripper can deal with two or three females before adding milt.

For the inexperienced worker, who may break a number of eggs, it is best to use a salt solution instead of water, pouring into the bowl enough to cover all the eggs that will subsequently be added. The reason is that when eggs are broken, globulin is released (*chapte*r 7) and precipitates in fresh water. This precipitate can block the micropyle, thus preventing penetration of the sperm and reducing the fertilization rate. Salt water will keep globulin in solution so that the micropyle is not blocked.

Despite the fact that the wet method is more usual, the fertilization rate obtained with its use is lower than an experienced stripper can obtain using the dry method. To some extent this is because the sperm remain active for several minutes in ovarian fluid, but are immobilized very quickly in water.

When using the dry method it is best to strip a male into the container first, followed immediately by a female. Subsequent stripping should be in the ratio of roughly one cock to thrce hens, though the number of cocks used depends on the amount of milt obtained – it is not readily obtainable from all. Several males should always be used in case any are infertile. From time to time, milt and eggs should be carefully and very gently stirred with the hand or a finger.

Stripping is a technique that comes only with practise. First try to find someone who can demonstrate the technique. If that cannot be managed, it will mean resorting to trial and error, and that will almost certainly result in killing or badly damaging some of the fish until sufficient experience is obtained. If practice is necessary on a mature fish, it is best to anaesthetize it, both for its sake and yours: trying to strip a slippery, struggling three year old fish is not easy, and without skill it can be very difficult indeed.

The eggs in a hen trout are packed in a fluid, the ovarian fluid, in membranous folds of the abdominal cavity. They emerge from the vent, from which excretory products are also voided. It is as well, therefore, to starve the stock for three or four days before stripping in order to empty their guts and so avoid too much in the way of faecal contamination of the egg bowls. It is impossible to avoid it completely: any large chunks that get in should be lifted out with the finger while stirring the eggs.

If eggs break loose in the body cavity because of clumsy handling of the fish, it will not be possible to recover them. They will be resorbed by the hen unless there are too many of them, in which case she will die. Although it is difficult when lifting a fish out of a net, try not to hold a ripe female head down – at least, bring her head up again as soon as possible. Head down, the eggs may slide forward in her body and will be irrecoverable.

To strip a hen grasp it very firmly indeed with the right hand round the peduncle (that part between the tail and the anal fin) in such a way that the head is to your left and the vent faces downwards and away from you. A glove or piece of coarse cloth should be used to get a good grip, otherwise the fish will twist away from you (*Fig 66*). Keeping her head up, use the left hand to grip the fish just below the pectoral fins (*Fig 67*). If you have the fish in the correct position you will find the middle knuckle of your right forefinger is more or less adjacent to the rear point of the anal fin. Use the left hand to support the weight of the body of the fish, keeping the left hand above the right at all times so that the head of the fish is always higher than the

Fig 66. Diagram of a trout showing fins and peduncle.

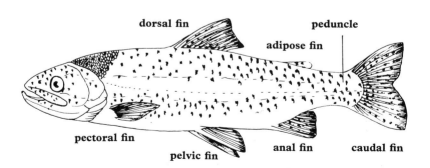

dorsal fin   peduncle
adipose fin

pectoral fin
pelvic fin   anal fin   caudal fin

tail. Momentarily squeeze the belly of the fish gently but firmly with the left hand, so that the urine squirts out. Direct it away from the egg bowl and from your fellow workers. Thrust your left leg forward, placing the left foot in such a way that the left thigh is thrust out from your body and forms a support for the fish and your own left arm. (*Fig 68*)

At this point you should have the hen firmly grasped by the peduncle with your right hand, and your left forearm should prevent the fish from thrusting the main part of its body upward. Your left thigh forms a platform for the whole manoeuvre. Your left hand should enclose the under side of the fish's abdomen, between pectoral and pelvic fins – rather more towards the pectorals. Hold the fish ventral (lower) surface down, vent pointing towards the bowl. With the whole of the palm, exert a gentle but firm pressure round the belly of the fish, squeezing a little towards the vent rather than the head. The finger tips

97

Fig 68. Starting to strip a hen. Note position of hands.

Fig 69. Squeezing out the last eggs from a hen.

should be just below the lateral line of the fish, on the one side, and the base of the thumb just below the lateral line on the other. Hold the hand still, but continue to exert firm pressure. Eggs should be extruded into the bowl. Try to make sure they do not come out so fast that they break. As they emerge, continue to keep up the pressure. In a moment or two the majority of the eggs will have emerged. As you feel the volume inside the fish diminishing, and the flow of eggs becoming more gentle, move the hand down towards the pelvic fins, exerting pressure now with the thumb and fingers as well as with the palm. Massage the eggs down towards the vent, preferably with one single movement, using reasonable pressure. Then, using fingers and thumb, continue with a number of short massaging movements from just above the pelvic fins down towards the vent, to get out the last of the eggs (*Fig 69*). As you are working, you should be able to feel the eggs moving, and you will know when the fish is spent.

When handling a ripe female, one of the more important points to remember is to exert the first pressure just a little behind the pectoral fins, so that the main bulk of the egg mass is forced down inside the body, towards the vent. As the eggs are ejected, the body of the fish will begin to feel flabbier in your hand. Try not to break the eggs by letting

Fig 70. Stripping a cock.

them spurt out too hard against the side or bottom of the bowl. The vent should be held fairly close to the bowl.

The operation does not take as long to complete as it does to describe, nor is it as complicated as it sounds when you have done it a few times. If you have to do it on your own, without guidance, try out the movements first with a dead fish – any size will do, of half a kilo or over. After that, try it out on a small live fish. There will, of course, be no eggs or milt, nor will you get the feel of the eggs inside the body, but you will become more accustomed to the way of handling a live fish, picking it up and holding it firmly so that it lies, without being able to struggle, in the correct position.

A little blood will often be seen during egg extrusion. Do not worry about it. If the fish have been starved, there should be little in the way of faeces, though a drop or two may be forced out during the last moments of egg shedding. If at this time the eggs have not all been forced out, wipe away the faeces from the vent and continue stripping.

When you have finished, put the fish carefully back in the water. Do not throw it, and do not mix it up with those awaiting stripping.

Males are stripped in much the same way, though in this case the pressure is principally between the thumb on one side of the fish and the fingers on the other (*Fig 70*). Massage gently but firmly backwards, just below the lateral line, from behind the pectoral fins down to the vent. It is not necessary for a large quantity of milt to be extruded. One drop will fertilize about ten thousand eggs.

The outline procedure given above applies to a right handed person who prefers to do the massaging with his left hand. Many do. It is a matter of personal preference which hand you use.

An experienced stripper will be able to handle a lively three year old hen in about thirty seconds, but if older fish are stripped, they may be too much for one person to manage, in which case they should be held by one worker and stripped by a second.

So long as the sperm are alive and fertile and the eggs receptive (*ie* with open micropyle), fertilization is practically

Fig 71. Bowls of fertilized eggs ready to be taken into the hatchery.

immediate (*Fig 71*). Later, the fertilized eggs should be washed with one or two changes of hatchery water to remove excess milt and debris. When the washing water comes away clean they can be placed carefully in incubation trays.

7 Hatchery practice

Egg development Trout eggs are spherical with a thin, porous elastic shell which is to some extent translucent, allowing the embryo within to be seen (*Fig 72*). A hole in the shell, the micropyle, permits entry of the male spermatozoan, which fertilizes the egg (*Fig 73*).

Inside the shell is the yolk sac, which encloses the yolk on which the developing embryo feeds. Situated on the yolk sac is the microscopic germinal disc, containing all those hereditary components of the future fish that are contributed by the female. After entering the egg, the male spermatozoan fuses with the germinal disc, thus contributing the male components. Fusion of the two initiates development of an embryo that will grow into an adult fish which, as well as resembling both parents in all essential details, will also differ from each in one or more minute aspects which, as is the case with all living animals, confer on it those individual characteristics that make it at one and the same time unique, yet typical of the species.

The shell of the newly emerged trout egg is soft, rather limp, and tends to be sticky. As it absorbs water, it swells and in a little while becomes hard and firm. As soon as it is fully expanded, the egg loses its stickiness, which was due to the porous shell absorbing water and thus tending to create a vacuum around itself, so that adjacent objects

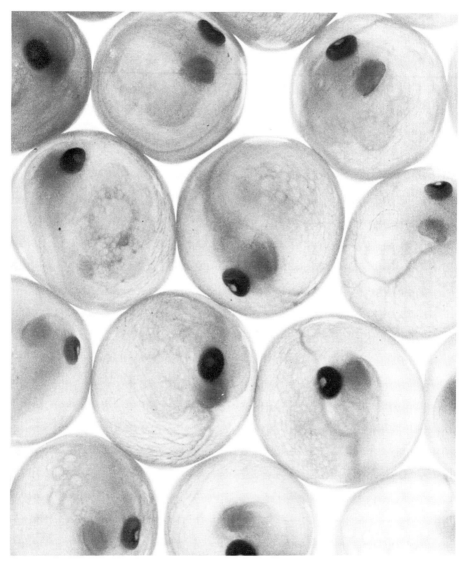

Fig 72. Eyed eggs.

become sucked in towards the surface. (The same sort of effect is obtained if a rubber ball with a small hole in it is squashed and then allowed to expand. If a thumb is placed over the hole as the ball swells, ball and thumb are inclined to stick to each other).

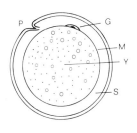

Fig 73. Diagram of trout egg
P: micropyle.
G: germinal disc.
M: yolk sac membrane.
Y: yolk.
S: perivitelline space, allowing developing embryo and its yolk sac to rotate within the egg.

Expansion of the egg takes about twenty minutes, and starts immediately it contacts water. During the first few minutes of this process the micropyle, caught between layers of egg membranes, becomes distorted, and closes. Consequently, it is imperative that the sperm should enter the egg immediately, before expansion has had time to close the door to it. That is the reason some hatcherymen prefer the dry method of stripping, keeping the plastic egg bowl dry and stripping sperm into it first, so that when eggs are added fertilization takes place at once.

Dead eggs are white because they contain precipitated globulin. This is a protein which is soluble in salt solutions, and while in solution is colourless. If there is insufficient salt in the solution, globulin cannot remain dissolved and precipitates out as a white solid. The egg yolk, held within the yolk sac membrane, contains a number of substances among which are salts and globulin. If the yolk sac membrane is damaged, or if it decays, the salt gets out and passes through the egg shell into the surrounding water. The result is that the salt concentration within the egg drops to a level at which the globulin precipitates, and the egg turns white. A small experiment can be carried out, in which a few dead eggs are placed in a salt solution for half an hour or so. They will become translucent, because the globulin has re-dissolved.

The incubation period of trout eggs, held at a known average temperature, varies considerably. Those taken from one female will probably hatch at much the same time, but those stripped from different hens on the same day may vary in hatching time by as much as five or six days, though if the hens were sisters the difference will not be great. In general, eggs held at 15°C hatch after roughly 20 days, though at the more usual hatchery temperature of about 10°C they will take about 30 days. At 4°C, if they hatch at all, they take about 100 days. If the water temperature fluctuates, hatching time can only be approximated. Temperature readings should be taken and recorded at least twice a day and an average calculated, though the figure obtained cannot be used with accuracy to estimate the hatching time unless there has been very little

Table 3. Number of days
from fertilization to
hatching

Water temp (°C)	Number of days to hatch	
	Rainbow Trout	*Brown Trout*
4·5	80	97
6·0	—	77
7·0	49	61
10	31	41
11	—	35
12	—	27
13	24	—
15	21	—

fluctuation about the mean (see *Table 3*).

Eggs will hatch at 18°C, but not much above it, and a constant temperature of 4°C will cause some mortalities. However, if the temperature has not dropped below 5°C before the eggs have eyed, they may survive and hatch at temperatures below 4°C. In cold climates it is probably worthwhile to install some form of water heating, sufficient to raise the temperature by a few degrees.

These figures indicate that, with experience, hatching time can be predicted to within a day or two with a reasonable degree of certainty, and in temperature-controlled incubator systems with considerable accuracy.

Unless breeding experiments are being carried out, eggs of wild fish should not be introduced into a farm, as there can never be any certainty about their state of health. However, some rivers in some countries are less likely to be infected than others and it is best to take a view based on a common-sense assessment of the situation.

Egg handling Eggs must be handled carefully. There are periods during their development when they are less susceptible to damage than at other times, but there are also periods when they should not be handled at all, or even jarred. They should never be handled roughly.

Newly fertilized eggs will stand a certain amount of manipulation, but after they have been exposed to water and the hardening process has begun they should not be interfered with again for at least another 20 minutes.

After that, they may be carefully handled for about 48 hours, but they then become very delicate again and should be left severely alone until they are eyed.

Abrupt temperature changes should be avoided. The temperature of the water in the basin containing the fertilized eggs should not differ by more than $1°C$ from that in which the eggs are finally placed. The temperature difference can be gradually adjusted by adding water little by little to the basin from the hatchery supply, until temperatures are equated. After that the eggs should be floated – not poured – into their baskets, or decanted with great care into bottles. In a basket they should not be more than two layers deep, though the capacity of a basket is usually stated by the manufacturers.

From roughly 48 to 72 hours after hardening there begins a process during which eggs become increasingly susceptible to damage. This, of course, is during the initial period of development of the embryo, when shock of any sort can disrupt the processes going on in the egg. Until they become eyed (which takes place about half way through the incubation period) they should be interfered with as little as possible. While in this delicate stage they are referred to as 'green eggs'.

The eyed stage is reached when two little black dots, which are the pigmented retina of the embryo's eyes, can be seen through the egg shell (see *Fig 72*). After this time they can be handled, shipped, and generally prepared for hatching.

Eggs which appear normal may be infertile. After they have reached the eyed stage they should be shocked. This can be done in a number of ways, the simplest being to tip them from one receptacle into another, allowing them to drop about 20 or 30 cms. Some workers prefer to stir them, and another method is to siphon them out into a bucket, which must have a screened overflow to prevent the eggs being lost. The shock, however it is administered, will rupture the yolk sac membrane of those that are infertile, causing them to turn white, when they can readily be recognized and removed.

Dead eggs in trough baskets should either be siphoned

off or disinfected because if they are left in the basket they will almost certainly become fungused, and the fungus will spread to the live eggs and alevins and kill them. Siphons may be home made or bought from a supplier of equipment.

Some farmers prefer to disinfect the trays by passing malachite green (which must be zinc-free) over them at a concentration of 2 ppm for one hour. This involves a continuous drip into the water flowing through the trough, or a constant siphon device; and the appropriate concentrations have to be calculated. On a rather more primitive basis, $1\frac{1}{2}$-2 gms of zinc-free malachite can be dissolved in 2·5 litres of water and 50-60 ml of this solution poured very slowly into the head of the trough, and another 25 ml half way down, once every two days. Too much malachite will damage the developing embryo, and some farmers prefer not to use it for this reason. The green dye is liable to get all over the place – treat it with respect.

If battery incubators or bottles are used, egg picking is out of the question and malachiting is the only answer.

If eggs are being bought in they should immediately be disinfected on arrival with an iodophore such as Buffodine or Wescodyne, to get rid of surface germs. Wescodyne may be used at a concentration of 1:300 in hatchery water, and Buffodine at 1:100. It is best, however, first to prepare a buffer solution by dissolving 0·1 gm of sodium bicarbonate per litre of hatchery water and using this buffer solution to dissolve the disinfectant. Eggs should be totally immersed in the disinfectant for not longer than ten minutes, then washed with four or five changes of hatchery water before being put in their baskets.

When the deep yellow colour of the disinfectant solution fades and becomes pale it will no longer be active and should be disposed of. Stocks of disinfectant should not be held for longer than a year; after that, they should be discarded and replaced.

Although harmless to man, iodophores are highly toxic to fish and must be used with great care. On no account must they be discharged directly into a stream or river. A concentration of 1:20,000 is lethal for fish. Take care that none is allowed to get into the farm water supply.

Eggs should also have been disinfected prior to despatch from the suppliers, as this safeguards not only the eggs themselves but also the material in which they have been packed. Nevertheless, the packaging is always potentially infected and should be burnt immediately and not left lying about. It should not be re-used.

Fry After hatching, the alevins (yolk-sac fry) (*Fig 74*) drop through the meshes of the basket into the water below. In some designs, however, with circular instead of elongated apertures, they remain in the basket until they are put out into fry tanks. In the case of those which drop through, a little very gentle assistance -- carefully shaking the basket a little -- will often be appreciated. Once in the water, they continue to feed on their yolk sacs for some time, usually for 2-6 weeks, depending on the temperature. They do not need much attention, though the trough or tray should be kept clean and dead fish and debris removed. Baskets containing nothing other than egg shells should be removed, disinfected and cleaned ready for the next batch or for storing. Egg shells should be siphoned off from baskets in which alevins are still emerging. All screens must be kept scrupulously clean. Some hatcherymen stop malachiting as soon as alevins begin to emerge; others keep on with it but at less frequent intervals.

As the yolk sac is absorbed, the fry become more active, and just as it can no longer be seen they begin to swim up to the surface, when they are commonly known as swim-up fry. At this stage it is important that the depth of water in the trough should not be more than about 10 cms, as the fry swim up to the surface to fill their air bladders and to feed, and if the water is too deep it is difficult for them.

This is a critical period in the life of the fish, because if feeding does not commence within a few days they seem to lose the will to take food, and consequently die. However, it is immaterial whether they are fed immediately they swim up, or whether feeding is delayed for a day or two – different opinions are expressed by different farmers. It is probably best to offer a little food, dribbling it gently between thumb and forefinger onto the surface of the water,

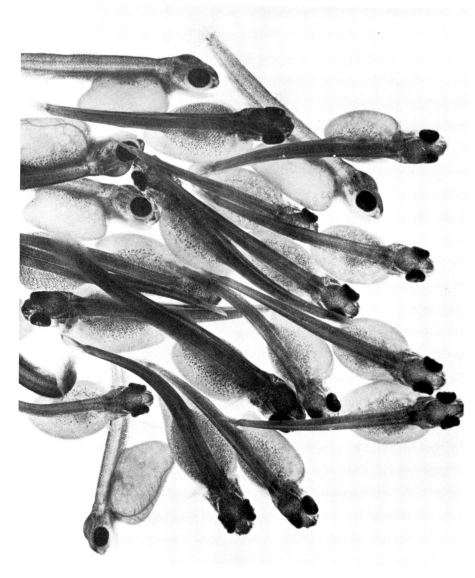

Fig 74. Alevins.

to see how they react. If they do not take it, try again a few hours later. Sometimes they seem to want a little encouragement, and must be treated with tolerance, sympathy and patience.

Rates of feeding and pellet size for first feeding fry are recommended by food manufacturers. Fry at this stage of their lives should always be well fed, but uneaten food should not be allowed to accumulate in the trough.

Many farmers prefer to hand feed at least ten times a day while the fry are still very young but, as this practice is obviously labour-intensive, automatic feeders are popular. They can be set to provide small amounts of food continuously, or to distribute monitored amounts at set times. Nevertheless, it is essential to keep a watch on the fish and the best way to do this is to hand feed two or three times a day, setting the feeders to carry out the job for the rest of the time.

Do not allow the trough to become fouled with uneaten food – sweep it out through the screen or siphon it off.

Incubator trays with swim-up fry on the point of taking food should be carefully immersed in fry tanks or raceways, and the fish allowed to swim out. Do not pour them out. Fry held in troughs need not be transferred to tanks until they are feeding well which, in the case of brown trout will be about 28 days at 10°C, and in that of rainbows, 21 days after hatching.

If troughs are not needed for any other purpose – and particularly if they are, they must be thoroughly cleaned and disinfected – it is convenient to leave about a third of the fry in them, moving the remaining two thirds to fry tanks. However, swim-up fry seem to enjoy being crowded to some extent, though it is of course important not to overcrowd them. A density of about 10,000/m² of tank surface is acceptable.

At about a month old, fry tanks can be stocked at up to 25 kg/m³ at a through-flow of 1 litre/min/kg. With a poor through-flow – perhaps a complete replacement of water in the tank 6 times per day – the stocking density would have to be reduced to 10 kg/m³ at most. Too high a stocking density reduces the growth rate and consequently increases the relative cost of food: in other words, it increases the CR.

On no account must fry be transferred to mud ponds until they are at least twelve weeks old. Prior to that time their bones have not hardened, and they are susceptible to attack by the parasite *Myxosoma cerebralis*, which causes whirling disease (see *chapter 9*). After bone formation is complete, the parasite cannot penetrate it, and they are safe.

Lastly, it must again be emphasised that light damages eggs, alevins and swim-up fry. Adult fish, too, should have some shelter from direct sunlight, particularly in hot climates. Trout have no eyelids, and cannot close their eyes, nor can they alter the diameter of the pupil. In nature, there is usually protective vegetation for them to shelter under, but on the farm they cannot escape.

Their dislike of light may, however, be usefully employed in moving fry up or down a trough for cleaning. If a 100 watt bulb is suspended a metre or so above the top of the trough, at one end, the fry will swim down to the other end and the part from which they have moved can be attended to. The light can now be taken down to the other end, and the procedure repeated.

Packing and despatch
Before packing, eggs must be shocked and those that are dead removed. Dead eggs can be picked off with a siphon, or they may be separated by the salt flotation method. Common salt is often used, and the method will be described for this substance. A tray in which a hatchery basket can be fitted is filled with water, salt added, and the solution stirred until the salt has dissolved. The volume of water and quantity of salt are noted for reference. A number of live and dead eggs are placed in the solution and the salt concentration adjusted until the dead eggs, which are less dense than those that are alive, float and the live eggs sink. The dead ones can then be skimmed off with a hand net. A hydrometer can be used for measuring the specific gravity of the solution, but it is better to have noted the quantities used because the strength of the solution will vary according to the age of the eggs and the time that has elapsed between shocking and salting. Some farmers assert that salt has an adverse effect on trout eggs, and prefer to use sugar or magnesium sulphate.

Photo-electric egg sorters are available either for purchase or hire, and are well worthwhile for hatcheries dealing with large numbers of eggs. They work on the basis of a beam of light shining through an aperture and stimulating a photo-electric cell situated opposite it. Live eggs, being translucent, cause only a minor diminution in the amount of light received by the cell, while dead eggs are opaque and block it. The cell operates a mechanism that directs white eggs one way and live ones another.

Eggs are usually packed in insulated containers in which the egg boxes are arranged in vertical stacks (*Fig 75*). The top box in each stack can be used for ice for long distance transport, though it is not necessary for local deliveries except in hot climates.

Prior to packing, eggs must be counted. The easiest way is to place a number of eggs on a plastic board with raised edges and an aperture at one end, and count them off into a container such as a cup, or a measuring cylinder of some sort. The number of eggs in the cup is known and it can be used to count the remainder, if the top layer is carefully evened off each time. A measuring cylinder is more accurate. The reverse method of filling the cylinder with eggs, up to the mark, and then counting them is obviously equally good. Either way, the container is known to hold a certain number of eggs when filled to the mark, and can be used as a measure when filling egg boxes for transport. It is just as simple – perhaps simpler – to weigh the container on a small spring balance. Eggs, so long as they are the same size, can then be sold by weight.

Fig 75. Box for egg transport. Note trays with compartments. The box lid is on the left.

Good trout eggs should be at least 5·2 mm in diameter. Fish hatched from large eggs grow more quickly than those from small ones.

8 Biology

Classification In terms of zoological classification, the brown trout *Salmo trutta* and the rainbow trout *Salmo gairdneri* both belong to the family Salmonidae, which in its turn forms a part of the order Isospondyli. As the name implies, all fish belonging to this order have vertebrae that are more or less equal in length. They also have the swim bladder connected to the oesophagus by a duct, the so-called pneumatic duct, and the pelvic fins are situated posteriorly, on the abdomen. The order contains a number of sub-groupings, from which the family Salmonidae can be distinguished by the presence of a small, fatty 'adipose' fin on the hinder part of the back, between the dorsal and caudal fins.

The brown trout is a native of European waters. Owing to its popularity with anglers it has been introduced into many countries in both northern and southern hemispheres, and has now become extensively distributed throughout many of the fresh waters of the world.

It seems possible that all present day trout are descendants of migratory species that originally inhabited the arctic waters, various groups having been isolated from time to time by changes in the terrain resulting from the movements of glaciers during the ice ages.

Whatever the reason, *Salmo trutta* is a species highly variable in superficial appearance; the colouring, and to some extent the shape, differs according to where it is found. Generally speaking, it can be said that if these varieties are moved to different locations, their appearance alters and, in angling terms, they are 'spoiled'. Since the pattern and colouration depend at any rate to some extent on dietary as well as hormonal influences, the latter of which are activated, perhaps, by visual stimuli, it is not altogether surprising that an environmental change will alter the appearance.

There seems to be a genetic element in the difference between freshwater brown trout and the race known as sea trout, which smolt and migrate to sea in the same way as salmon. According to Frost and Brown (*see Appendix*), quoting other authorities, sea trout reared in a fresh water environment retain the migratory instinct in the first generation, but lose it in the second. It would seem, therefore, that whatever genetic difference there may be is by no means persistent. Perhaps all brown trout have inherent in their genetic make-up the physiological capacity to smolt, this attribute coming to the fore, possibly over a couple of generations or more, in those whose environment presents them with the opportunity to contact brackish or salt waters. This, however, is pure surmise: zoologically, sea trout and brown trout are both *Salmo trutta*.

The rainbow trout is a close relative of the brown trout and in general anatomical and physiological terms differs very little from it. However, the two species are genetically distinct, the offspring of crosses being infertile.

Rainbow trout were originally natives of the rivers draining into the Pacific from northern Mexico to the Kuskokwim River in Alaska but, like brown trout, they have been so widely distributed by man that they are now present in many of the freshwaters throughout the world. Further, owing to their suitability for intensive farming, they have been extensively cross bred and it is doubtful if many pure races exist. There is a considerable amount of disagreement between taxonomists as to the status of the different varieties that have been described. Early spawners were thought to be a different species to late spawners,

114

those spawning in the autumn and early winter being labelled *Salmo shasta* and those spawning in late winter to spring being grouped as *Salmo irrideus*. These names – shasta and irrideus – now remain in use only as convenient terms by which to refer to early and late spawners. However, farmed stocks in temperate climates usually spawn from autumn to early spring.

As is the case with brown trout, there is a migratory race of rainbows. These are known as steelheads, and bear very much the same relationship to rainbow trout as sea trout do to browns. In the Sacramento River, upstream migration takes place from July to the middle of the following March, with a peak during September and October. Spawning is from December to April. Movement downstream occurs maximally in the spring, usually at night. This is also the case with introduced stocks of brown trout in the western United States of America. Both sea trout and steelheads return to their home river in the same way as salmon but, unlike salmon, do not usually move far from the coast.

Rainbows can be differentiated easily from brown trout, with experience, at a glance; but if there is any difficulty, rainbows have spots on the caudal fin (tail) and an irridescent band along each side of the body, a band that becomes more obvious at spawning time. At this time, too, the lower jaw of the males of both rainbow and brown trout develops an upward curving hook or 'kype'.

Anatomy and physiology Although for descriptive and analytical purposes it is convenient to consider the various anatomical regions of the trout as separate entities, in practice they cannot be separated and it is important to realize that although every cell in the body of a living organism behaves to some extent as an individual, carrying out those functions for which it has become specialized, the body is nevertheless an integrated whole, each cell and each organ system acting and reacting with other systems, so that a dynamic balance is maintained.

Skin and scales The skin of trout consists of an outer epidermis and an inner dermis. Unlike that of mammals, the epidermis is a thin layer of living cells, some of which are specialized for the purpose of producing mucus, which is continually manufactured and is the substance that makes the trout slippery when handled. It covers the whole of the body surface, protecting it from attacks by fungi and bacteria. Some authorities assert that it reduces friction between skin and water, but others disagree with this view.

Below the thin epidermal layer, the cells of the dermis secrete the bony scales which form a flexible, protective covering, the top of one scale overlapping the base of the next. On hatching, trout are devoid of scales, which begin to develop when the young fish is about 2·5 cms in length and can be discerned when a body length of 4-4·5 cms has been reached. They are seen first of all in the lateral line region, subsequently spreading dorsally and ventrally to cover the body. The scales themselves do not contribute much to the colouring of the fish, changes in which are due largely to physiological mechanisms. The skin contains cells known as chromatophores, which have long, wavy finger-like processes and contain pigments. Optical stimuli result in hormonal changes which bring about contraction of the pigment into the centre of the cell so turning it into a small spot, or cause its expansion along the cell projections so that it becomes very obvious and causes a distinct colour change in the fish. The dark pigment, melanin, may assume a brown hue when expanded and carotenoid pigments, which are red, may appear orange or yellow. Such changes, superimposed on the basic pigmentation of the skin, provide a wide variety of colours and spots which are complemented by the deposits of guanin crystals which, when present, cover the scales. These crystals are known as iridocytes, and are a waste product of metabolism. Differences in iridescent colour are due to reflection and refraction of light by iridocytes lying above a reflective layer situated below the scales.

Skeleton and fins Since trout live in water, a medium of much the same specific gravity as the fish, there has been no development of a massive skeletal and muscular system designed to overcome the gravitational forces which land animals expend a great deal of energy in resisting. Instead, evolution has resulted in a structure capable of exerting strong propulsive forces able to drive the body through a dense environment.

The skeleton consists basically of the skull, the backbone, the radial skeleton and the bones to which the pectoral and pelvic fins are attached.

The skull is formed of bony plates cemented together to produce a structure that protects the brain, houses some of the organs of special sense, and forms the jaws. Without going into too many details, the upper jaw may be said to form the bottom of the skull. It consists of an outer bone which is toothed and, internal to that and parallel to it, another toothed bone, so that immediately inside the mouth is a double row of teeth. In the middle of the upper palate, running backwards from the point of the snout, is a third toothed bone. All the teeth are pointed and directed backwards, so that prey are held firmly but cannot be cut or chewed. In any case, no sideways movement of the lower jaw is possible, and there are no flat, grinding surfaces on the teeth. The outer bones forming the mandible, or lower jaw, are similarly toothed.

Attached to each side of the rear of the skull, and forming a part of it, are the grill arches, which are part of the bony support for the gill filaments. Also attached to the rear part of the skull are the upper parts of the bones forming the pectoral girdle which supports the pectoral fins.

The backbone is attached to the rear of the skull and consists of a series of vertebrae, held together by ligaments and connective tissue. Although similar in essential structure, the vertebrae differ in detail as they progress backwards from the head. All consist of a central bone (the centrum) which bears above it a bony arch, the neural arch. Through the channel formed by the succession of arches runs the spinal nerve cord which, in the skull, is developed into the brain. That part of the neural arch projecting above the canal is known as the neural spine. Towards the tail, the centra also bear a lower projection, the haemal arch, through which run blood vessels supplying the kidney.

Immediately behind the head the vertebrae bear ribs which form a cage to protect the majority of the internal organs. The vertebra immediately behind the head is not moveable, and movement is much restricted in those bearing the ribs. Further back, however, the vertebrae move easily from side to side. The rearmost vertebrae connect with the rays of the caudal fin.

Inset in the dorsal musculature are bones forming a part of the radial skeleton. Known as the interneurals, they intercalate with the spaces between the neural spines lying below them and, above, with the dorsal fin rays.

The posterior ventral part of the musculature is also inset with a similar series of bones forming another part of the radial skeleton. These are the interhaemals, which intercalate with the haemal arches above and the rays of the anal fin below.

Floating, as it were, in the musculature of the ventral surface of the fish, just in front of the vent, are one or two small bones forming the pelvic girdle and supporting the pelvic fins. It is these bones which, as a result of evolution, have developed to form the pelvic girdle of the mammal. They have never become properly articulated with or supported by the spine and, although the arrangement is moderately satisfactory for land mammals that run on four legs, those that stand erect on their back legs, like man, cannot be said to be well constructed in this region, since the main bulk of the body is supported by bones that are only inadequately attached to it. The arrangement results in many aches and pains.

The head of the trout is considered to be the whole of the skull and its attachments as far back as the gill arches and opercula. The trunk is the rib region and the tail is that part of the body lying behind the rib cage. Posteriorly, it bears the caudal fin which, in common parlance, is often referred to incorrectly as the tail.

In addition to the caudal, there are seven other fins: two pectorals, one on each side of the body; two pelvics, again one on each side; a median anal fin on the ventral surface just behind the vent; and a median dorsal fin more or less centrally placed on the back with a small adipose fin behind it also medial in position. With the exception of the adipose whose function is unknown, all the fins are supported by bony rays.

The dorsal and anal fins prevent yawing and rolling. The pectorals play a part in movement in an upward and downward direction as well as assisting in turning and in backward movement. Moreover, they can be extended and opened to act as brakes, an operation that results in a lifting force being exerted on the fish. This can be counteracted by the pelvic fins which also to some extent prevent rolling. The caudal fin increases the length and area of the propulsive part of the body of the fish, and thus assists movement.

Although such manoeuvres are primarily the functions of the fins, the eyes and ears play an important part in the maintenance of balance and alteration of direction and movement. Also involved is the swim bladder, a thin-walled sac lying immediately below the kidney. Gas may be passed into it by swallowing air at the water surface and driving it by movements of the buccal cavity (mouth) along the pneumatic duct into the swim bladder. Alterations in the volume of gas in the bladder result in concomitant changes in the specific gravity of the fish, so that it can remain more or less motionless without effort at any required depth in the water. The hydrostatic function of the swim bladder plays an important part in the ability of the fish to move easily upwards or downwards and adapt to the different pressure of the water at different depths. In trout, the gas in the bladder consists principally of nitrogen, with a little oxygen and carbon dioxide. It is often observed that the pneumatic duct is blocked with mucus, and therefore cannot always function in the way described. The walls of the swim bladder are plentifully supplied with blood vessels, so that gaseous exchanges can easily be made between the capillaries and the bladder. In this manner the swim bladder can be inflated or deflated without recourse to the pneumatic duct and it seems probable that this, in fact, is the more usual method of controlling its volume.

Musculature   Although it may not always be obvious, all vertebrates and a great many invertebrates are made up basically of a number of similar segments which, during development, become modified, fused or overlapped so that it is extremely difficult or impossible to delineate them in the adult animal. A caterpillar is an example. Its segmentation, at any rate in the body region, is easy to see but what is not so obvious is that its head also consists of a number of fused segments, one bearing the eyes, another the jaws, another the minute antennae.

The segmental musculature in the trunk region of a fish is easily seen if the skin is stripped off. Each myotome or muscle segment follows a zig-zag dorso-ventral course across the body, the muscle fibres themselves running in an antero-posterior direction between the fibrous tissues that separate each myotome from the next. The musculature of any one segment is attached to projections of the corresponding vertebral centrum. From the central nerve cord that runs in the canal formed by the neural arches, segmental nerves transmit impulses to the relevant muscles and receive messages from the sensory nerve endings of that segment. Since, as has been said, the segments shift during development, the nervous supply also shifts, so that in the adult the primary segmental disposition becomes obscured in many parts of the body.

To return to the trunk region and its myotomes, a wave of contraction passing from trunk to tail will result in a swing of the tail in a sideways direction which forces the water backwards and so propels the fish forward.

Muscles moving other parts of the body such as the jaw, fins and eyes are, as has been said, segmental in origin but have become adapted and moved to carry out special tasks.

The musculature that has been described is under the control of what are known as voluntary nerves, and its contraction is a consequence of conscious or reflex activities in the central nervous system.

There are two other types of muscle: smooth muscle is responsible for movements of many internal organs such as the peristaltic contractions that flow down the length of the intestine, squeezing the food and driving it back towards the anus. This type of muscle is under the control of the autonomic nervous system. Its operations cannot consciously be changed. The third type of muscle is that which operates the heart. It differs from both the other types in that it beats automatically, of its own volition, nervous stimuli serving only to alter its rate.

Intestinal tract and digestive system (see Fig 76)

The mouth leads into a pharynx from which gill slits open into the respiratory chamber. From the pharynx the oesophagus, into which opens the pneumatic duct from the swim bladder, leads into the U-shaped stomach, the posterior end of which, the pylorus, is surrounded by a circular muscular valve, the pyloric sphincter. The pylorus opens into the small intestine, and into this region there also open a large number of small blind-ended tubes the pyloric caeca, which produce digestive enzymes. More digestive enzymes are poured into this part of the gut by way of the pancreatic duct from the pancreas, and the digestion of fats is facilitated by bile juice, which is produced by the liver, stored in the gall bladder and

Fig 76. Diagram of trout anatomy.

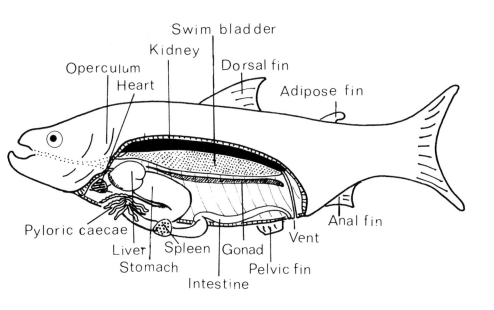

delivered into the upper intestine by the bile duct. This array of substances that break nutrients down into their component parts is heavily supplemented by enzymes secreted by the glandular epithelium of the intestine itself.

From time to time, the pyloric sphincter opens, liberating a quantity of partially digested food from the stomach into the lumen of the intestine in which, as it is pushed gradually backwards by the peristaltic contractions of the muscles surrounding the gut, it is subjected to the combined activities of the chemicals already described.

The food is thus digested, carbohydrates being broken down into their component sugars, proteins into amino-acids and fats into fatty acids and glycerol. These relatively small molecules are taken up by the cells forming the intestinal lining, from where they are passed into blood capillaries which lie in intimate contact with the cells. The blood then passes through a special system (the hepatic portal system) to the liver. Indigestible remains of the diet pass down to the rectum, where they are compacted. When a sufficient quantity has been accumulated, the anal sphincter opens and the waste is voided to the exterior.

The nutrients arriving in the liver are further broken down in the tissues of that organ, and re-assembled into those particular molecules that are suitable for the fish, and can be used to build up or replace the cells and tissues of all parts of the body. Some fats and carbohydrates are stored, but too much fat cannot be dealt with and results in fatty deposits in the liver which may cause malfunction.

Excretory system As has been seen, gross waste in the form of undigested food fragments are voided by muscular contractions of the rectal wall which force them out through the anus. This procedure, however, is not generally considered with the excretory processes, which are concerned with ridding the body of useless or toxic chemicals resulting from cellular metabolism; that is, the chemical reactions that take place in the various types of cell that constitute the tissues of the body.

Ammonia, which is a toxic end-product of amino-acid metabolism, and consequently of the breakdown of proteins, is excreted by specialized cells in the gill lamellae. Other nitrogenous compounds and many other waste products are carried in the blood stream from the body cells to the kidney which, in the trout, is a long organ extending throughout much of the body length of the fish. It is situated immediately below the spine and to some extent protected by small downward projections of the vertebral centra. It is covered with a thin, colourless membrane.

The trout kidney consists of two parts, the anterior or head kidney, and the posterior kidney. These carry out very different functions, the head kidney being concerned with haemopoiesis (*see Fig 76*), while the posterior kidney functions as the principal excretory organ.

The small blood vessels that ultimately bring the blood into the cells of the kidney tissues end up as a specialized mechanism that filters the waste, together with some valuable dietary components, into the kidney tubules, the cleansed blood returning to the venous system of the fish. The tubules themselves are provided with another blood supply into which are passed, by the activity of the tubule cells, those important substances which have escaped through the filter, but which need to be re-absorbed. The tubules themselves join to form a series of ducts which eventually discharge into the ureters, a pair of canals lying alongside the kidneys. The ureters fuse porteriorly, and discharge to the exterior by way of the vent.

One of the functions of the kidney tubules is, when necessary, to reabsorb water, but in order to discuss this it is first of all necessary to consider osmosis.

A semi-permeable membrane is one that is permeable to some substances but not to others. Some semi-permeable membranes will allow the passage of pure water but not of salts dissolved in it, and it is this type of membrane that makes up a great many of the tissues of trout.

If a strong salt solution is present on one side of such a membrane, and a weak salt solution on the other, water will pass through the membrane until the concentration of salts on both sides is equal. The passage of water through the membrane in this way is known as osmosis.

The concentration of salts in the body of a trout is greater than the concentration of salts in fresh water. The consequence is that water tends to pass into the tissues of a trout in fresh water, principally through the membranes lining the gut, and those of the gills. As a result, trout in fresh water tend to become waterlogged and therefore excrete large quantities of very dilute urine, no water being re-absorbed by the kidney tubules.

On the other hand, the concentration of salts in sea water is greater than that in the body of the fish, so that water tends to diffuse out and the trout becomes dehydrated. However, salt water is drunk and absorbed through the intestinal epithelium. The salts are excreted through specialized cells in the gill lamellae, and the kidney tubules re-absorb the majority of the water passing through them, so that the water content of the body is maintained.

The physiological changes associated with a change from fresh to salt water can be appreciated, and explain the stresses to which fry are subjected when transferred from a freshwater tank into a sea cage.

Head kidney and spleen It was noted on page 123 that the head-kidney is concerned with haemopoeitic activities. Haemopoeisis is the assembly and break-down of blood components. Both anterior kidney and spleen – a blackish or dark red body loosely attached to the bottom of the U of the stomach – are concerned with the production of blood substances in addition to the manufacture of red and white blood cells. The spleen is also concerned with breaking down worn out blood components. Both are heavily supplied with blood vessels which connect with sinuses in the tissues of head kidney and spleen – sinuses in which the various reactions take place.

Nervous system and sense-organs The central nervous system of the trout consists of a long spinal nerve cord which runs from head to tail through the channel formed by the neural arches straddling the vertebral centra.

The spinal cord itself consists of nerve cords giving off branches peripherally, in between each neural arch, to the tissues of the body. Some of the branches are motor nerves terminating, for instance, in muscles, and controlling their contraction. Others are sensory nerves receiving messages from the sensory endings in the tissues, passing these messages back into the central nervous system and thus initiating appropriate responses that are transmitted in the motor nerves. While many of these responses are reflex – that is, the incoming message automatically triggers a motor response – others are conveyed to one part of the brain or another, where they are analysed prior to involvement of the motor nerves which will initiate the appropriate action.

The brain consists of a number of lobes, each concerned with the processing of different stimuli. A detailed description would not be helpful.

Incorporated in the spinal cord is the autonomic nervous system which has previously been mentioned.

All sensory nerve cells, such as those of touch and pressure, play an important part in the survival of the fish in its environment, since they convey information about contacts with the outside world as well as about the internal state of the body and its functions. However, there are a number of special sense organs that convey particularly important impulses. In the trout, these are the eyes, the olfactory organs, the taste buds in the mouth, and the acoustico-lateralis system.

In trout, taste perception is uniquely confined to the receptors in the buccal cavity, and is not blended with the sense of smell as it is in land animals, where the olfactory passages connect with the back of the mouth. The nostrils are blind ended sacs provided with sensory nerve endings stimulated by chemicals dissolved in the water. The impulses are transmitted to the olfactory lobes in the fore-brain.

The eyes are essentially similar to those of mammals, but in detail are different. The eyeball is more or less spherical, and filled with a colourless fluid. Its transparent front forms the cornea, behind which is the iris, a circular ring of tissue with, in the centre of it, a hole which is the pupil. The iris is not capable of expansion or contraction, and the size of the pupil cannot therefore be altered. Immediately behind the iris is a spherical, transparent lens. At the back of the eyeball lie very large numbers of sensory nerve cells receptive to light waves. These form the retina, and become prominent quite early in the development of the embryo within the egg. They are the two black dots seen in eyed eggs.

Light passing into the eye through the cornea and the iris is focussed on the retina by the lens, which can be moved, by muscles, backwards or forwards in order to bring it nearer to or further away from the retina as necessary in order to obtain an accurate focus.

The ear of the trout is contained in a cavity in the skull, and forms the anterior part of the acoustico-lateralis system. There is no outer or middle ear, as there is in mammals, the fish ear corresponding only to the mammalian inner ear. It consists of an upper part which is formed of three semi-circular canals filled with a fluid which tends to remain static as the ear is moved, so that receptor nerve endings in the canals are stimulated by the apparent movement of the fluid. The canals are orientated in the two lateral and the one horizontal directions of three-dimensional space, so that movement of the trout in any direction is perceived and fed into the auditory lobes of the brain.

Below the semi-circular canals are hollow, fluid filled sacs, primarily concerned with the reception of the pressure waves that are interpreted by the brain as sound.

The lateral line – the other part of the acoustico-lateralis system – consists of a hollow, fluid filled channel running the length of the body, one on each side, from ear to tail. It is easily visible as a slight depression in the body of the trout.

The channel communicates by way of a series of pores with the body surface, so that pressure changes in the water are passed to the fluid in the channel. These changes stimulate organs known as neuromasts, which consist of a group of nerve cells supplied with a hair like projection. The neuromasts connect with a nerve cord running below (interior to) the channel, and this, in turn, conveys impulses to the brain.

These stimuli are believed to convey to the fish the

movement of the water around it, as well as pressure differences emanating from movements of nearby objects, such as other fish. In this way, the trout may be made aware not only of the presence of possible predators or prey, but of the direction in which they are moving, as well, possibly, as the speed. Since the range of vision is not great in a dense medium such as water, particularly in the dark or at depths to which light does not easily penetrate, and more particularly if the water is clouded, such a system may be essential for survival.

<table>
<tr><td>Respiratory and blood systems</td><td>The branchial (gill) arches have previously been mentioned in connection with the skull. Articulating with each bony arch is a double series of very small bones which are regularly spaced down its length, sticking out at right angles to the arch. These small bones are the gill rays. Each is moveable on the arch by means of muscles, and each ray supports the tissues of a gill lamella, so that the gill lamellae can be moved and a greater or lesser surface of epithelium exposed to the circulating water in the gill chamber. The primary lamellae are themselves folded, each fold constituting a secondary lamella. Thus, a very large epithelial surface may be presented to the water.</td></tr>
</table>

The lamellae are richly supplied with blood capillaries, and since the surface epithelia form an extremely thin layer, there is almost instantaneous passage of gases between water and circulating blood.

The gill arches lie in the branchial cavity which is covered by the operculum (gill cover). This is attached to the skull, to which it is hinged so that, being free at the bottom and the posterior edge, it can be opened or closed. Passage of water over the gills is controlled by movements of the mouth and the opercula. If the mouth is opened and its floor lowered while the opercula are closed, water will be drawn into the pharynx. If the mouth is now closed and the opercula opened while the floor of the mouth is raised again, the water is driven over the gills and swept out through the opercular opening. The probability is that controlled movements of this type result in a more or less continual passage of water through the mouth and pharynx, out through the gill slits, over the gills to discharge by way of the opercular opening.

The heart, which is situated in the pericardial cavity just below the pharynx, pumps venous blood up through the capillaries of the gills, where the carbon dioxide it contains is exchanged for oxygen. The resulting arterial blood passes forwards to the head and backwards to the other regions of the body. The arteries become arterioles as they penetrate the tissues they supply, and terminate in capillaries which are in intimate contact with the cell surface. Since nutrients are also carried in the blood stream, these, as well as oxygen, are transferred to the cell, whose waste products, including carbon dioxide, are passed out again into the blood in the capillaries, which eventually fuse to form venules and then veins which return the blood to the heart.

In the tissues, blood fluids as well as white cells and other components may pass out of the capillaries into the tissue spaces, where they form the so-called tissue fluids. These fluids drain into an extensive system of thin-walled vessels known as lymphatics, which convey the fluids, the lymph, back into the main venous return to the heart.

Endocrine system Nervous regulation of the body is assisted by chemicals known as hormones, which are secreted into the blood by endocrine glands and are thus carried to the site of action. While the nervous system is concerned with immediate responses to stimuli, the endocrine system is responsible for longer term processes such as growth, sexual maturation and reproduction, as well as many of the adaptations and reactions to changing environmental conditions and maintenance of the general equilibrium of the numerous metabolic activities of the trout.

The endocrine glands are to a very large extent inter-dependent, each functioning or its activity being repressed by the products of another, with the result that the whole system is in a constant state of dynamic flux.

The pituitary, which is situated above the buccal cavity and below the midbrain, is concerned with sexual maturation and reproduction, osmoregulation and the control of the chromatophores of the skin. It also regulates the activity of the thyroid gland, whose hormones are concerned with growth and development. The adrenals (which in fish are separated into somewhat diffuse groups of cells, some of which are in the head kidney) produce sex hormones and adrenalin, as well as many other steroids whose functions are unknown. The gonads themselves contain endocrine cells which secrete sex hormones, and it seems probable that these cells are under the control of the pituitary.

There are several other endocrine glands in the trout, but their function is not clear.

Reproductive system   The ovaries of the immature female trout are two rather granular strings of cells lying in the body cavity dorsal to the gut. As they develop and eggs begin to form, they become more obvious and eventually become two masses on each side of the body on each side of and above the intestinal tract. The eggs are supplied with nutrients from certain cells in the ovaries. The ovary itself is contained within a thin membrane which ruptures when the female is ripe, so that the eggs become loose in the body cavity and can be squeezed out through the vent. The structure of the eggs is described in chapter 7.

The genital products of the male, the spermatozoa, are produced in the tissues of the smooth, white testes, which occupy a corresponding position in the body to the ovaries of the female. The spermatozoa are carried in a white seminal fluid, the milt, which can also be pressed out of the vent of the ripe male. Each spermatozoan is a minute organism which moves by means of a protoplasmic whip-like projection, the flagellum. Spermatozoa, like eggs, contain only half the normal number of chromosomes so that when the egg is fertilized the full number is made up, each parent contributing a part of its genetic make-up to the embryo that will develop.

Life cycle   In nature, spawning of both rainbow and brown trout occurs on the gravelly bottom of a suitable stream. A nest is 'cut' by the female, usually in the presence of males who do not, however, take any part but content themselves with fighting for possession of the female.

Vigorous body movements of the female result in a saucer shaped depression. When this has been completed and the hen has 'tested' it by feeling it with the region of her anal fin, she inserts her vent into the bottom of the nest. Her head now higher than her tail, her mouth opens and the male moves alongside, quivering, also with open mouth. Eggs and milt are extruded simultaneously. The male moves away, but the female covers the eggs with gravel by movements of her caudal fin.

Simultaneous production of eggs and sperm is essential, since sperm can exist in water for only a minute at most. They are actively motile organisms and are presumably attracted to the egg by some chemical stimulus. One sperm enters the egg by way of the micropyle, which is immediately closed, thus preventing entry of a second sperm.

The rate at which the eggs develop depends very much on the water temperature (*chapter 7*), but 8°-12°C is about optimal.

The first positive sign of incipient hatching is seen when the two black dots which are the two retina of the developing embryo can be discerned. This is known as 'eyeing' (*see Fig 72*).

When the embryo is ready to hatch, the outer shell layers are dissolved by enzymic action, the embryo remaining in the inner membrane from which it eventually breaks free as a result of vigorous wriggling. At this stage the remainder of the egg yolk is still attached to the gut of the fish, and remains so until the food supplies within it are exhausted.

Alevins avoid light by wriggling under the stones that form the nest, but when they have finished the remains of the nutrients in the yolk sac they seem to be temporarily attracted to light for a brief period, and swim up to the surface. At this time it seems probable that they gulp atmospheric air to fill their swim bladders. Afterwards, light is again avoided, but the fry, which by now are about 2·5 cms in length, turn their heads to the current, swimming actively against it and so at least maintaining their position.

At this stage they are very much at risk. The scales have not developed, and it is doubtful if there is any immunity to disease. They are highly susceptible to attack by both predators and parasites and a large number die before feeding is started. Further mortalities occur later, so that only one or two per cent of the eggs ever reach maturity under natural conditions.

The survivors continue to develop, the rate at which they grow depending on a number of factors which include the length of the day, temperature and availability of food. At this stage, the skeleton of the young fish is cartilaginous and soft. It can thus be penetrated by the parasite *Myxosoma cerebralis*, the causative agent of whirling disease (*see chapter 9*). Farmed fish should be kept in tanks until their cartilage has been replaced by bone, a process that will have been completed by the time they are three months old. The parasites will then be unable to penetrate the cranium, where they do the damage. The reason for keeping fry in tanks while they are still susceptible is because the parasites, once an infection has occurred, persist in the mud of earth ponds.

The earliest age at which male rainbow have been reported as sexually mature is nine months, but this is abnormally early. A number mature at one year but, at any rate on farms, the more usual age for stripping is two or sometimes three years. Females have been reported mature at twenty two months, and many farmers strip at two years, though the eggs at this time may not be as large as those obtained from three year olds.

9 Parasites and disease

There are several books on fish diseases, some better than others. One or two of those recommended are listed in the appendix. Articles on hygiene and disease in aquaculture systems are often printed in fish farming journals and have the advantage of being up-to-date.

In this book it is not intended to deal with specific diseases, but to provide for the layman a certain amount of background information on what diseases are, why they occur, how they affect the fish, and what can be done to prevent or cure them.

The descriptions and explanations that follow are directed at fish farmers who may not be acquainted with scientific jargon, so that where it is necessary to use technical terms they will be defined either in the text or the glossary.

Transmissible and non-transmissible diseases

There are two principal types of disease: transmissible and non-transmissible. These are otherwise known as infectious and non-infectious.

Non-transmissible diseases are caused by a large number of factors such as malnutrition, poor environmental conditions, congenital or inherited defects in the structure or functioning of the fish itself or, far too commonly, incompetent husbandry. In many cases diseases of this sort constitute a management problem which can be overcome by changes and improvements in farming techniques. Fish kills, which are often caused by de-oxygenation or gross contamination of the water, come into the category of non-transmissible diseases, as do continuing mortalities due to a constant minor degree of contamination. If fish are accumulating quantities of a slow-acting toxin within their bodies, the picture presented will be similar in many respects to that resulting from a chronic transmissible disease, and may initially cause diagnostic difficulties.

Transmissible diseases are caused by parasites. A comprehensive description of the term 'parasite' would be at best boring, so here it will be described as a living organism that spends most of its life on the surface of, or inside the body of another living creature which, for obvious reasons, is known as the 'host'.

Unfortunately, and illogically, the term 'parasite' is used by biologists to refer specifically to relatively large organisms such as *Argulus* and *Gyrodactylus* and others which can be seen fairly easily either with the naked eye or a low-power lens. Very small organisms like bacteria and viruses are not generally referred to when speaking of 'the parasites', but are usually spoken of simply as bacteria or viruses. Nevertheless, they are important parasites and in the present volume, when the word 'parasite' is used, it refers to any organism, however large or small, which fits the description given earlier.

The various types of parasites affecting fish are described in considerable detail in more than one of the books listed in the appendix, but all the literature is to some extent uncommunicative about viruses which, if they are referred to at all, are usually only very briefly noted. However, viruses are very different from bacteria, with which they are often confused. A knowledge of these differences is useful in the practical treatment and management of diseases on a fish farm.

Bacteria are minute, unicellular plants. Each single cell divides into two, and each resulting daughter cell again divides. This process is repeated, so that a very large number of offspring can arise from one parent cell. Under

133

optimal conditions, some bacteria are capable of dividing every twenty minutes, so that in about eight hours one single bacterium can give rise to nearly seventeen million offspring. As dying or newly dead fish provide a suitable environment for bacterial growth and reproduction it will be seen that it is wise to remove them from the pond as soon as possible.

Bacteria can also undergo a form of sexual reproduction in which there is an exchange of genetic material which ultimately results in some slight divergence in the characteristics of the offspring, so that eventually different 'strains' of the species appear. Since these strains differ slightly, either in structure or function or both, from the parent strain, they can cause trouble and difficulties in the production and use of vaccines. They may also vary in their susceptibility to chemotherapeutic agents.

The body of an animal such as a fish is composed of cells. Cells of one particular type form a tissue (*see Fig 77*) such as nervous tissue or epithelial tissue, and various tissues combine together to form an organ, such as the liver or kidney. The tissues themselves, and the cells of which they are made up, are bathed in a fluid which is appropriately known as tissue fluid, which carries nutrient substances to the cells and takes away their excretory products.

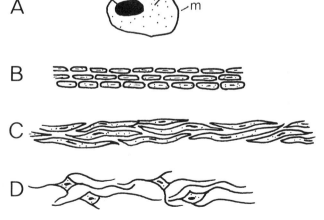

Fig 77. Diagrammatic representation of a cell and tissues.
A: a cell, nucleus, cytoplasm, cell membrane.
B: epithelial tissue.
C: muscle tissue.
D: nerve tissue.
Note the different cell types that make up individual tissues.

134

These fluids, as well as the blood itself, are those in which bacteria live when they invade the body of the host. Most bacteria do not live inside the cells, but outside them, in the tissue fluids. There, they absorb nutrients which, by right, should have contributed food to the cell; and into the tissue fluids they excrete their waste products, which can be poisonous. And when bacteria die and disintegrate, some of the products of their disintegration may also be poisonous. It can be appreciated, therefore, that bacteria constitute a very serious interference with the normal life of the cells of the host's body, and it is this interference and the damage that results from it, that ultimately shows itself as the signs and symptoms of disease.

In human medicine, signs of disease are what can be seen of it, either directly or by means of tests: ulcers, opaque eyes, bloody patches or spots are all signs. Symptoms are what can be told by the patient: pain, nausea, depression, headache, for instance. Fish, however, are not noted for their ability to communicate with humans, and it is usual to refer to all indications of disease in fish, as symptoms.

The majority of bacteria can live and reproduce outside the body of the host so long as the fluid in which they find themselves contains the necessary nutrients, and many can continue to exist for some time in extremely adverse conditions, so they may be difficult to eradicate from the environment as well as from the body. Other bacteria, however, have to be provided with nutrients normally found only inside a living body: these are the obligate pathogens.

All viruses are obligate pathogens. They cannot reproduce themselves, but they impose their own genetic mechanism on that of the cell they infect in such a way that the 'coding' of the normal machinery of the cell is altered, so that instead of producing cell substance, the cell itself produces virus substance. It is a peculiarly sophisticated form of parasitism. The subsequent fate of the cell depends on whether its production of virus destroys it completely, or whether it can continue to live and at the same time continue to provide viruses. In the first case, the cell disrupts, releasing virus particles in large numbers; in the second, virus particles are released from time to time until the cell eventually dies. In both cases neighbouring cells will probably become infected, so the virus spreads through those body cells it is able to penetrate. Viruses do not absorb nutrients, they are incapable of reproducing themselves and they do not carry out any of the normal activities of living organisms. In the usually accepted sense of the word, they are not alive. They simply exist. Perhaps one of the easiest ways of indicating that bacteria differ fundamentally from viruses is to point out that bacteria themselves may suffer from virus infections.

The relationship of bacteria and of viruses to the body in which they are living is therefore superficially similar but, in reality, quite different. Bacteria are living organisms feeding on substances similar to those on which the cell feeds. Viruses, on the other hand, are merely organic particles which fuse intimately with the cell they infect and, to all intents and purposes, become an integral part of it. The consequence is that bacteria can be individually damaged by exposure to drugs, but viruses cannot; if the virus is damaged, so is the cell in which it lives.

Chemotherapeutic drugs
Chemotherapeutic drugs such as sulphonamides incorporate substances which are probably best thought of as selective poisons: they damage the metabolic activity of the bacterium without damaging that of the host; they can be mixed with the food given to the fish, or they can be administered in any other way that will enable them to be incorporated into the nutrient substances circulating in the tissue fluids – substances on which both body cells and bacteria feed. The bacteria will be poisoned, but the body cells will be relatively unharmed. Antibiotics function in a somewhat similar manner, and have more or less similar effects. Unfortunately, it is clear from what has been stated previously that virus diseases cannot be treated in this way. Nevertheless, they can often be prevented by good management and competent husbandry, and some can be avoided by enhancement of the natural defences of the living fish by means of immunization techniques such as vaccination.

Administration of chemotherapeutic drugs or of antibiotics must be carried out with care. If too small a quantity of the drug is given, some bacteria may survive and their progeny, some of which may also survive in the presence of the drug, could give rise to a resistant strain of the organism unaffected by the drug. Resistant strains of this type will obviously be more difficult to deal with in future outbreaks of the disease.

It is also undesirable to administer too large a quantity of the drug since, although its effect on the host is small compared to its effect on the bacterium, it may nevertheless produce undesirable consequences. The dosage of any such drug is always a compromise between the rate at which it damages the infecting organism, and the rate at which it damages the patient.

There follows a list of some of the more common infectious diseases of trout, together with brief references to the diagnostic signs exhibited by the fish, and a few notes on transmission and treatment.

Only a limited number of responses to physiological disturbances can be made by a trout, and only a handful of these are visible to the naked eye. There is consequently a good deal of overlapping of visual symptoms between one disease and another, and diseases due to nutritional disorders or adverse environmental conditions may present signs similar to some of those seen in infectious conditions.

Very much more detailed descriptions of trout diseases may be seen in Roberts and Shepherd (see appendix), but the information given here may assist on a preliminary level.

Virus diseases

Infectious pancreatic necrosis (IPN)

Usually affects very young fry after feeding has started, but may be seen in fingerlings up to about six months old. Both rainbow and brown trout are susceptible.

Signs are: a sharp increase in mortalities; darkening of the skin; abdominal, distension; erratic swimming and pop-eye.

Infected adult fish as well as survivors of an outbreak may carry the disease without showing any sign that they are infected. The disease is also carried on the surface of eggs as well as inside them, so that although disinfection of the eggs will help to reduce the number of virus particles present in an infected shipment, it may not eliminate all of them.

Viral haemorrhagic septicaemia (VHS) The most susceptible group is rainbow trout of 5-25 cms in length, though older or younger fish are occasionally affected. Brown trout are probably resistant. The disease is seen at temperatures below 14°C, usually from 6°-12°C. It can cause extensive losses in fish of marketable size.

There are three stages of the infection:

(*1*) Acute   Signs: sudden increase in mortalities; trout gather along the banks of a pond or at outlets; darkening of the skin; pale gills, sometimes with bloody spots: occasionally, bloody patches at bases of fins, and a tendency to pop-eye.

(*2*) Chronic   Follows the acute stage. Signs: skin becomes almost black; gills very pale; marked pop-eye; continued mortalities at decreased level.

(*3*) Nervous   This is the last stage of the infection. Signs: a marked decrease in the number of fish affected; swim in spirals, death following.

Survivors of an outbreak carry the virus for the rest of their lives, and can transmit it. Egg infection is not nearly as common as in IPN, and the virus is not present inside the egg.

Infectious haematopoietic necrosis (IHN) This disease is usually confined to trout under one year old. Two year olds are not susceptible. Occurs at temperatures under 15°C. Both brown and rainbow trout are affected.

Signs: sudden increase in mortalities; darkening of the skin; pale gills; pop-eye; a degree of abdominal swelling, not usually marked; long, trailing faecal casts from vent, and small bloody patches at fin bases. Transmission as for VHS.

Treatment of virus diseases No therapy possible. In the case of IPN, the infection is usually important only in young fry, and if hatchery and fry tanks are on a pure water source infection is unlikely. Eggs should be obtained from certificated sources, or from those known to be free of the disease. Since VHS occurs only at temperatures below 14°C it can be eliminated if it is possible to hold the fish at a temperature in excess of this. IHN infections can similarly be controlled or prevented by holding stock above 15°C. However recent research throws doubt on the efficacy of these preventive measures.

If none of these husbandry solutions is possible, a remission of the disease may sometimes be obtained by reducing the stocking density. This is particularly the case in IPN: placing the fry in a much larger volume of water can markedly decrease the incidence of infection. All sick and dead fish should be removed promptly and buried in lime. Other preventive methods having failed, the only solution is to kill the entire infected stock, bury them in lime, thoroughly disinfect all holding facilities such as tanks and raceways, leave them fallow for at least a month, re-disinfect, flush out very thoroughly several times and re-stock.

Bacterial diseases
Furunculosis

This disease affects all age groups of all salmonids, and has been reported from marine farms. Brown trout are more susceptible than rainbows.

Outbreaks are usually seen when the water temperature rises, particularly if the fish are overcrowded.

There are two forms of the disease:

(*1*) Acute — Few external signs, often none. Characteristically, a sudden onset, with high mortalities, no apparent sign of disease.

(*2*) Sub-acute — Gradually increasing mortalities, with bloody patches on the body, particularly at fin bases; development of large ulcers.

Survivors of an outbreak, or fish infected by other means, often carry the causative bacterium but show no sign of infection. Introduction of such fish into a stock will frequently produce an outbreak when the water temperature rises. The bacterium is probably carried on the outside of the egg.

Vibriosis

Very similar to furunculosis. Generally affects fish cultured in salt water, but is also fairly common in fresh water.

139

Treatment of infection is carried out by decreasing stocking
density in warm water and disinfecting incoming eggs.
Also the following may be mixed with the food:

Sulphamerazine:	200 mg/kg fish/day.
Tetracycline:	75 mg/kg fish/day.
Furazolidone:	75 mg/kg fish/day.

Initiate treatment as soon as the infection is confirmed.
Sick fish will not feed, and consequently will not take the
drug.

Protozoan diseases
Whirling disease

Affects alevins, fry and fingerlings up to about six months
old. Signs: darkening of the skin; spinal deformities;
swimming with a fast, whirling motion.

Infected fish can carry the disease and transmit it by
liberating the organism into the water, where it persists in
mud. Trout under six months of age should, therefore, be
kept in clean tanks or raceways, and should not be transferred to mud ponds until they are older. Sick and dead
fish should be taken out of the water and buried in lime.
The holding facilities should be disinfected and left fallow
for at least two weeks. Disinfection of mud ponds is
difficult, and not likely to be entirely successful.

Costiasis

Affects brown and rainbow trout of all ages, and at all
temperatures.

Signs: listlessness: resting in slack water; lying on the
bottom; flashing; often a blueish film over the body
surface, and lack of appetite. The parasite, which can be seen
at a magnification of x40, may be found on the body
surface or gills.

Treatment by immersion in a formalin bath, at a final
concentration of 200 ppm for a period of $\frac{1}{2}$-1 hour, depending on the age of the fish and the degree of infestation, is
often effective. In water temperatures of over 12°C the
concentration should be reduced to 150 ppm. In both cases
the water must be aerated, as formalin absorbs oxygen.
Repeat the treatment if necessary. Persistent damaging
infections should be eliminated by destruction of stock and
disinfection.

Ich (Whitespot)   This disease affects trout of all ages at all temperatures.
Signs: small white circular spots on the body surface;
flashing; scraping.

The parasite cannot be treated on the fish, but treatment
with zinc-free malachite as a daily routine for a fortnight,
at a concentration of 1 ppm for one hour may help, though
continued malachite treatment is not to be recommended
as a general rule. Remove sick and dead fish and bury in
lime. Keep the tank clean by daily sweeping.

Disease caused by a   A small worm known as a 'Gyro' (*Gyrodactylus elegans*) may
parasitic worm   affect fingerlings and growers at medium water
temperatures.

Signs: flashing; scraping; general irritation. The
parasite is usually seen when conditions are unhygienic.

Treatment is by means of a formalin bath (see *Costiasis*).

Fungus disease   External damage by wounding, parasites or diseases
Saprolegniasis   affecting the skin may result in saprolegnia infection at any
age and any temperature.

Signs: Fungal patches and 'mats' or 'whorls' on the body
surface. These may be small and confined to the fin bases,
or may be extensive. In bad cases the trout will become
listless, lose its appetite and may die.

Treatment is a bath in malachite 1 ppm for one hour,
repeated if necessary (see *Ich*).

Natural defences   Internal parasites must be able to survive and reproduce
against infection   inside the body of the host they infect, while the host, in
this case the trout, has to defend itself against the attack of
the parasite.

The first and one of the most important defences of any
animal is its outer covering, its skin or shell. But in this
protective sheath there are gaps such as the soft coverings of
the respiratory surfaces and the mouth and intestinal canal.
These do not pose the same problems of penetration to an
invader as does the hard outer surface, and it is tissues such
as these that offer a door – a portal of entry – to many
parasites. It is clear, therefore, that there have to be internal
defences as well. Although these are complicated and

difficult to describe in detail, there are two important defence mechanisms that should be mentioned. They are both extremely effective and both have practical consequences for the fish farmer. One is connected with the 'carrier state' and the other with vaccination.

In the case of a disease such as furunculosis, caused by the bacterium *Aeromonas salmonicida*, the microbe penetrates the outer defences of the fish and finds itself in the tissues, bathed in the nutrient solution that percolates slowly among the cells forming the internal organs. Here, if not disturbed, the bacterium could simply sit and feed, reproducing itself when it felt inclined. From the fish's point of view such a state of affairs could not continue, since it would result in ever increasing numbers of bacteria, all utilizing nutrients which should have been for the benefit of the host, and all excreting noxious wastes. Furthermore, large numbers of the parasite would die, leaving an accumulation of disintegrating poisonous debris.

Even in a completely healthy and uninfected fish there is a continual breakdown and replacement of the cells of the body, and the debris from this natural process must be removed. This task is carried out by phagocytes, which are cells capable of ingesting other cells or fragments. They are the scavengers of the body. As well as being carried round in the circulating body fluids such as blood, they can move actively and can, for instance, push their way between the cells lining the blood vessels and so migrate out into the surrounding tissues. Phagocytes also form a lining to the surface of parts of some organs: for instance, to parts of the liver. If particles of broken down cells or foreign matter – and invading bacteria are most certainly foreign matter – come into contact with the phagocytes, they are ingested and destroyed. From the point of view of the bacterium, such a fate is undesirable, and most have their own methods of defending themselves. Some, however, have no defences and are immediately susceptible to phagocytic attack. Consequently, they do little damage to the host. At most they might cause a passing indisposition while they were being dealt with. Others have extremely efficient means of protection, are difficult to eradicate and, as a result, may cause a disease. Those which have no means of protecting themselves cause no disease and are therefore said to be avirulent. Others, those which can resist attack and damage the host, are virulent. The degree of virulence depends on the microbe's ability to survive and reproduce and cause damage in the face of the concerted attack of all the fish's defence mechanisms. Entry of quite large numbers of avirulent organisms – perhaps through a wound – will have little effect on the fish, while invasion by only a few highly virulent organisms may cause a severe disease.

Infective dose If a particularly virulent microbe, not at all susceptible to attack by the defence mechanisms of the fish, can penetrate the body, it will survive and propagate. In such a case the 'infective dose' of that particular microbe is said to be 'one', because one such organism will produce an infection and, when it has reproduced to a significant extent, it will cause a disease. A less virulent microbe may be able to persist in the fish only if several of them are able to gain entry. In this case, their rate of reproduction may be such that their numbers increase faster than the phagocytes can destroy them. To take an example, perhaps the phagocytes could deal with a few less than a million, but a few more than a million would just sway the balance and the phagocytes could not kill them quickly enough to prevent a gradually increasing bacterial population. In this case, the infective dose would be 'one million.'

The concept of infective dose has important practical applications in fish farm husbandry. The virus disease infectious pancreatic necrosis (IPN) affects young salmonids. For the sake of this argument (and only for the sake of this argument) assume there are a million particles of virus in each litre of water, and that a hundred thousand particles constitute an infective dose. There are, therefore, ten infective doses of virus in every litre of water. If there are ten fish per litre, each fish stands a chance of picking up an infective dose and each fish may therefore become diseased and die. But if the volume of water is doubled, the number of virus particles per litre will be halved. Each fish will therefore contact only fifty thousand virus particles, which is not an infective dose, and all the fish will survive.

Naturally, it is not as simple as that. There may not be an even distribution of virus particles or of fish; one fish may pick up an infective dose, become diseased, and excrete millions of virus particles, thus increasing the concentration; some fish may be stressed, and others not – there are a thousand and one things that may affect the situation. Nevertheless, this somewhat oversimplified account makes two practical points. The first is that if IPN is seen in the hatchery, an increase in the volume of water will lessen the chances of an epidemic. The second is that overcrowding increases the risk of disease.

One further point may be made: since a fish may be infected by numbers of an avirulent organism which are not capable of causing a disease, it is clear that, although the terms are used synonymously in common parlance, an infection is not necessarily the same thing as a disease.

Antibodies

To return to the inside of the fish and its defences: a second extremely effective mechanism is that of antibody production. This is another very complex matter which can, however, be simplified to some extent. Certain cells in the body produce proteins which, because of the way in which they function, are known as antibodies. For simplicity those cells will be called lymphocytes. Antibodies are produced by lymphocytes in response to stimulation of the lymphocyte by an antigen. An antigen is something – usually a protein – that generates production of antibodies. Since all microbes contain proteins as part of their structure, all microbes are antigenic, and therefore all microbes will induce lymphocytes to produce antibodies (*Fig 78*). Antibodies formed against one particular protein are unique to that protein, reacting uniquely with it and with no other protein. It is a lock and key situation. A good lock can be opened by only one type of key, and that key fits that particular lock and no other. All chemicals have atomic and molecular configurations, and proteins are chemicals. Each type of protein – and there are millions of them – has a unique molecular configuration. Antibodies produced by

Fig 78. Development of immunity. The bacterium (b) enters the body of the fish where it encounters lymphocyte (L) which is stimulated to produce antibodies (Ab) which react with corresponding antigens on the bacterium, thus inactivating it.

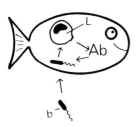

Fig 79. Production of specific antibodies. Two different bacteria with antigenic structures (G_1) and (G_2) are shown at the top of the diagram where they are reacting with lymphocytes (L_1) and (L_2) respectively, thus inducing the lymphocytes to produce antibodies specific to each type of bacterium. The specific antibodies thus produced (Ab_1) will not react with (G_2) and (Ab_2) will not react with (G_1). (R_3) and (R_4) show the two bacteria inactivated by the antibodies the lymphocytes have produced.

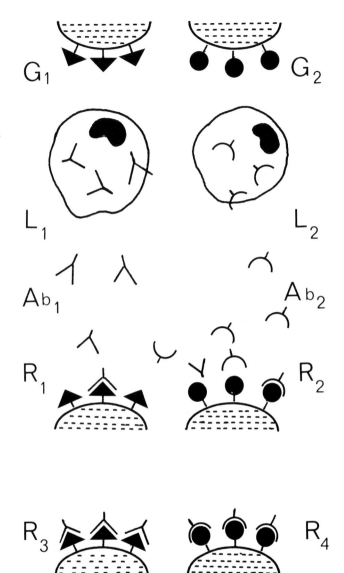

lymphocytes in response to stimulation by a protein will have a structure that will exactly fit the structure of that particular protein and no other. In a few words, the antigen will induce production of specific antibodies (*Fig 79*).

Therefore, when a microbe comes into contact with a

145

lymphocyte, antibodies will be produced which fit, specifically and exactly, the proteins on the surface of that type of microbe. The antibodies – which are very small indeed – will lock on the microbial proteins against which they have been formed, and will consequently alter the structure of the proteins. Because their structure is altered, they will cease to function efficiently. As these proteins form part of the microbe, the microbe itself will consequently be unable to function with full efficiency, and will die. In addition, and just as importantly, some antibodies are more palatable to phagocytes, so that microbes to which antibodies have become attached are not only killed by the action of the antibody itself, but are ingested much more easily by the phagocytes (*Fig 80*).

After the lymphocytes have been stimulated by an antigen, it takes them some time to produce antibodies in any quantity, because they have to go through a process which to all intents and purposes is the same as having to learn how to do it. In mammals, that process takes about ten days. In fish, the speed of the reaction depends to some extent on the water temperature, because the speed of all activities in a living body is affected by the temperature at which they take place, and the body temperature of a fish

Fig 80. Diagram of phagocytosis of bacteria by phagocytic cell. (A) and (B) are two identical bacteria. Phagocyte (P_1) is attacking bacterium (A) without much success. Meanwhile lymphocyte (L) is producing antibodies (Ab) as a result of stimulation by bacterium (B), and the antibodies are shown inactivating the corresponding antigens (g). Antibody-coated bacteria are being ingested with ease by phagocyte (P_2) and bacteria in process of being engulfed and digested are shown at (C) and (D).

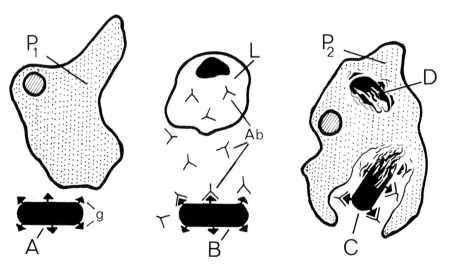

is not controlled, but is much the same as the temperature of the surrounding water.

To summarize what has been described: when a fish becomes infected – not necessarily diseased, just infected – its phagocytes do their best to kill the invaders. They may be completely successful and if so, apart from feeling a little off colour for a day or two while the conflict is going on, the fish will suffer no ill effects. On the other hand, the phagocytes may to a greater or lesser extent be overwhelmed by the number of invading organisms. If they are completely overwhelmed, the fish will probably die. If, however, they can manage to hold down the number of microbes until antibodies are produced, the whole picture will change and the fish will stand a good chance of recovery. Nevertheless, the activities of the microbes prior to their elimination may have damaged the fish to such an extent that it will not survive or, at best, will be permanently weakened.

There is another important possibility. Suppose an infection has been overcome, but the phagocytes have been unable to destroy the microbes they have engulfed. The pathogens will sit there inside the phagocyte, unable to do anything very much but still alive. Now suppose the fish is subjected to stress, perhaps by a rapid rise in water temperature. Things go wrong: possibly the blood supply to some part of the body is interrupted and the cells there, deprived of oxygen, disintegrate. Although another blood supply may quickly take over, there may meanwhile have been some destruction of those very phagocytes in which the pathogens – still alive – are held. The pathogens will be released and the fish, still under stress, will now be presented with a new invasion by the virulent organism it at first overcame but was not able completely to eliminate. What might have been only a minor disturbance to the fish's system caused by a rise in temperature has now turned into a major battle against the rapidly multiplying survivors of the previous attack. Not only is the individual fish once more affected, but the bacteria may pass out of its body, to be distributed through the water and picked up by other fish. Very soon, an epidemic will have started.

147

Fish carrying live pathogens in the way described or in other more or less similar ways, are appropriately known as 'carriers'. Introduction of carriers into a healthy stock will obviously present problems. They are often very difficult to detect since, under normal circumstances, they will show no sign of disease, and the number of pathogens carried may be so small that they are liable to escape observation even by laboratory methods.

Finally, another look at antibodies. It will be recollected that the lymphocytes which produce antibodies take a little while to learn how to do it. But once having learnt, they remember. The consequence is that when they are presented with a new invasion by microbes of a type they have previously overcome, antibodies in great concentration are rapidly produced, with the result that the disease does not develop. That is the reason that human beings are very rarely affected twice by illnesses such as measles or mumps.

Immunization   This capacity of lymphocytes to remember past encounters can be put to good practical use. Suppose a laboratory culture of *Aeromonas salmonicida* is treated in some way, perhaps with heat or a chemical, which will kill it without changing its normal antigenic configuration too much. That is, its capacity to cause lymphocytes to produce the usual antibodies against it will not be altered. To put it a little more technically, the pathogen will be inactivated but its antigenicity will be preserved. If bacteria killed in this way are inoculated into a fish (or, more practically, incorporated with the food) they will 'prime' the lymphocytes to produce antibodies against them, and these antibodies will be similar to those that would have been produced against live bacteria. The consequence will be that when, at some later time, the fish becomes infected naturally with the same strain of bacterium, the lymphocytes will remember their previous encounter, antibodies will be produced in abundance very quickly, and no sign of disease – or at least very little sign – will be seen.

That process, inoculation of the fish with a killed culture, is called immunization. The killed culture of the microbe is a vaccine.

Live vaccines are often more efficient than those prepared from killed cultures. To produce a live vaccine it is necessary to discover or to produce – there are a number of methods, all difficult – a completely avirulent type of organism. Unfortunately, avirulent strains are not always useful, since many of them will not induce antibody production against virulent strains. In addition, living organisms may change; an avirulent strain becoming virulent. The consequence is that very great care has to be taken in their production, and continuous test programmes have to be carried out in manufacturing laboratories in order to ensure safety of the product.

Since viruses cannot be treated with chemotherapeutic agents or with antibiotics, vaccines hold out the only real hope of prevention of virus diseases.

10 Transport

Whether borne by consignor or consignee, transport costs
are inevitably reflected either in the price of the product or
the profits of the producer. When buying or developing a
fish farm, one of the first considerations must be the
accessibility of the site, not only to the market but to
deliveries of essential consumables such as food and fuel.

Although deliveries to and from remote locations may be
made by air, this method of transport places a limit on the
weight as well as the bulk of shipments and will usually
restrict air transport to consignments of hatchery products.
In any case, there must be a reasonably good road from
hatchery to airstrip, passable at all seasons but more
especially during those in which deliveries of eggs, fry and
fingerlings are made.

Unless packages are to be accompanied – and, in most
cases, even when they are – detailed arrangements must be
made with the airline prior to despatch. Most firms are
helpful, doing their best to ensure speedy delivery of
perishables, but it is as well to come to a prior agreement
concerning responsibility for losses and whether this
devolves upon consignor, consignee or shippers, or their
respective agents, as well as defining at precisely what part
of the journey the responsibilities of one firm cease and
those of another begin. Insurance cover is desirable.

Arrangements also have to be made with the authorities in the country of destination. Health certificates may be required, and it is essential to expedite customs clearance. Although protracted correspondence may be tedious, all necessary formalities should be cleared and finalized, in writing, before shipment is undertaken.

Onward transport by road or air at the receiving end of the journey can usually be arranged by or through the consignee, though if delivery to the recipient farm premises forms part of the contract, the consignor or his agent will be responsible for the details. In this connection it is advisable to know the dates of public holidays in the country of delivery. Arrival of perishable cargoes at a time when no work force is available for the next two or three days can be catastrophic. It is also as well to try to keep abreast of industrial troubles in transport firms as these can also cause delays. Orders may have to be juggled around, perhaps making local deliveries of goods originally destined for shipment abroad and delaying those orders until a more suitable time.

It is sometimes wise for exporters to make sure the consignee is familiar with the technical procedures immediately following delivery, otherwise the producer may find himself blamed for mortalities that are, in fact, the fault of the recipient. For instance, eggs shipped in ice at a temperature of about 4°C may arrive at their destination in hot sunshine at a temperature of, say, 38°C. If they are exposed to such conditions for more than a few moments, they can be damaged. The boxes should not be opened in direct sunlight, and the temperature in the box should be adjusted slowly to correspond with that in the trough or tray into which they are to be transferred.

Methods Fry and small fingerlings can be shipped in plastic bags filled to one third of their capacity with water then blown up with oxygen and sealed. The first bag should be placed in a second, for added safety, and one or more bags can then be packed in a cardboard or, preferably, an insulated plastic container of suitable size. When practicable, fish can, of course, be shipped in ordinary insulated tanks provided with oxygenation facilities and, if necessary, refrigeration.

Deliveries of adult fish over short distances in temperate climates present relatively few problems, though the water must be oxygenated. For small to medium scale local deliveries, insulated glass fibre tanks of various sizes and designs are available (*Fig 81*). Usually they are rectangular, with rounded edges and corners, and can be bolted to a flat-bed truck or trailer provided with oxygen cylinders or aerators (*Fig 82*) from which a hose ending in a diffuser (*Fig 83*) is led into the tank. Oxygen cylinders should be firmly housed; they are heavy and can cause a great deal of damage if they break loose.

All tanks must be fitted with drain valves, and some are also fitted with a larger valve to which a wide-bore pipe can be attached and the fish flushed straight out. Some tanks are manufactured with fittings on which internal nets can be supported, so that they hang in the water. This provision is useful if transport is to be made over rough roads, as the netting prevents the fish from being bumped against the sides of the tank – something that can cause a considerable amount of damage that may not be obvious immediately, but which can result in mortalities after delivery. This arrangement has the additional advantage that the whole netful of fish can be lifted out with a small

Fig 81. Insulated transport tank mounted on trailer.

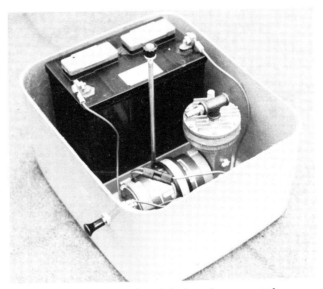

Fig 82. Battery driven aerator for connection to transport tank.

mobile crane and lowered straight into the water at the delivery site.

For local or long distance transport, larger sized tanks can be purchased, which can be fitted to flat-bed or drop-side trucks provided with electric pumps operated from a generator or heavy duty battery (*Fig 84*). Water is pumped from the bottom of the tank and sprayed in again at the top. A venturi may be fitted in the water circuit, to draw in air and aerate the water. In hot climates, however, this process may heat the water because of high air temperatures and, consequently, some models – usually those carrying more than 2,000 litres – are provided with a refrigerating coil at the top of the tank, over which the water is sprayed.

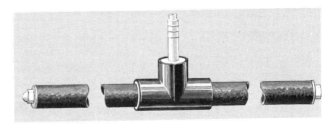

Fig 83. Diffusion block for transport tank:
  air supply at 5lb psi
  overall length 2ft

Fig 84. Flat bed truck fitted with insulated transport tanks.

For larger consignments, tankers are available with a capacity of 10,000 litres or more. They are provided with refrigeration and aeration or oxygenation facilities which are usually powered by a separate petrol or diesel motor. They may be ordered from specialist manufacturers, but are expensive both in terms of capital and running costs. Some are operated by government agencies, and by firms specializing in fish transport. Large consignments for delivery over long distances, particularly in warm climates, are best left to specialist firms.

Fish farmers making their own deliveries should ensure that all tanks are completely filled with water in order to minimize surging during transit. Larger sized tanks should be fitted with baffles.

Carrying density

The density at which fish can be carried depends on a number of inter-related factors. To take one or two examples, the temperature of the water in the tank affects its capacity to hold dissolved oxygen, and it also affects the oxygen requirements of the fish as well as their metabolic rate which, in turn, dictates the rate of excretion of urine, faeces and carbon dioxide. The faeces contain organic substances which absorb oxygen, and the urine contains ammonia which is toxic. If an analysis of the situation is necessary, all these and many other matters have to be taken into consideration, so it is difficult to make generalizations. What can be said is that the situation is improved if the fish are starved for a couple of days before shipment, so that their guts are empty and contamination of the water is consequently reduced.

It is probably safe to say that fingerlings can be carried in salt water at a density of 0·1 kg per litre, and in fresh at 0·15 kg per litre, since fresh water holds more oxygen than salt water. Portion sized fish may be transported at roughly twice that density because they metabolize more slowly; they can be carried at 0·2–0·25 kg per litre in fresh water, though at a rather lower weight in salt water. The weight per litre depends partly on the temperature of the water and the efficiency of oxygenation. The temperature should preferably be maintained at not much more than 5°C, and should not rise above 10°C. These figures apply for a journey of twelve hours. For shorter journeys the density can be slightly increased. In the case of very young fish oxygenation should not be overdone, as super-saturation of the water can result in gas-bubble disease.

All fish are stressed during transit, and additional stress should be avoided as far as possible. Fingerlings hatched in fresh water are sometimes delivered direct to marine farms and decanted straight into sea water cages, causing a double shock as a result of both osmotic and temperature changes. When practicable, the water temperature in the delivery tank should be equated with that in the recipient tank or sea cage by slowly draining the delivery tank and refilling it with the water into which the fish are to be placed. This procedure will to some extent prevent an abrupt temperature change, though it will not have much effect on the osmoregulatory trouble (*see chapter 4*). Fingerlings for delivery to sea farms may already have been acclimatized to sea water in the hatchery, though a sudden temperature change can still cause damage.

Weighing Assuming they have been recently graded, and after samples have been weighed and counted in the usual way (*Chapter 3*), fish may be weighed into transport tanks bin by bin or, for smaller numbers, bucket by bucket. They should be handled with care, as they are under stress during this process and will be subject to more stress during transport. If equipment is available it is preferable to pipe or pump them through wide bore hoses. Pumping into delivery vehicles can be undertaken more conveniently if a visual water gauge is fitted vertically to a convenient part of the tank, so that the water level inside can be read off. The sight gauge is calibrated by filling the tank with water and then lowering the level until it can be seen at the top of the sight gauge. Water is now drawn off in measured quantities. In order to do this a tub is placed on a balance and water piped into it until the weight has been increased by a given amount – say, for example, 50 kg. When the tub has come up to weight, a mark is scribed on the gauge. Another 50 kg is then run out from the tank into the tub and a second mark scribed on the gauge. Eventually, the gauge will thus be calibrated into 50 kg quantities from top to bottom. These measurements and scribings must be done accurately, and there must be no splashing of water which would invalidate the weighings. For deliveries, the water level is adjusted to the starting mark on the gauge, and fish are then netted or pumped in until the finishing mark is reached. For example, suppose 100 kg of fish are required. The water level is adjusted to the bottom mark and fish netted in until the water level reaches the 100 mark. However, it is necessary to know that the specific gravity of fish is a little higher than that of water, therefore they weigh a little more. On average trout weigh 1·02 times the equivalent volume of water, so that for every 100 kg on the gauge, 102 kg of fish will be delivered. The excess can be allowed for or charged or, for the sake of good relations, thrown in by the farmer to allow for any possible damage or losses during delivery. These calculations apply only to fish weighing more than 25 gms. *Table 4* gives the length to weight ratios of trout.

Table 4. Length to weight ratios of trout.	Length	No per	Weight of 1000
	(cms)	kg	in kg
	2·5	3300	0·30
	3·2	2650	0·40
	3·7	1875	0·68
	4·5	1100	0·91
	5·0	750	1·32
	6·5	385	2·59
	7·5	220	4·54
	9·0	145	6·85
	10·2	100	10·07
	11·5	66	15·10
	12·7	53	18·87
	14·0	35	28·35
	15·0	29	34·52
	16·5	22	45·36
	17·7	16	64·77
	19·0	12	90·72
	20·5	10	102·06
	23·0	7	142·88
	25·5	5	201·85
	28·0	3·6	273·97
	30·5	1·6	354·72

Water replacement   During long journeys, especially in warm climates, the water will have to be changed. Fresh water should be obtained from a previously arranged source, known to be pure and uncontaminated, and preferably saturated with oxygen. In order to prevent harm to the fish it is important that water changes should not be made abruptly, since the fresh water may differ both in quality and temperature from the old. About one third of the total volume of water in the tank should be discharged, and replaced from the new source. After about a quarter of an hour the process should be repeated. Lastly, after a similar interval, the tank should be drained as far as possible, leaving sufficient water in for the fish, and then completely re-filled. Care must be taken not to knock the fish about while the water is being replaced.

The condition of the fish should be examined from time to time during the journey. If they are seen to gasp at the surface a change of water will be necessary as soon as possible, but so long as they remain down towards the bottom of the tank all will probably be well. In an emergency, buckets full of water from any reasonable source should be poured in.

Foreign transport   When shipping fish across a continent, passing from one country to another, it is sometimes necessary to travel through intermediate independent territories, and this can present problems. There will almost certainly be customs formalities which can, in some cases, cause protracted delays. Although at many frontiers there may be no obstacles once customs have been cleared, in some cases further difficulties may be encountered. Health certificates may have to be produced at official water points, in order to control or obviate the discharge of contaminated water, and legislation may forbid discharge of waste or abstraction of fresh water at any other than authorized locations. There may also be formalities concerned with disinfection. If long distance transport of this sort is to be undertaken by the farmer himself, rather than employing a specialist, these and all other relevant details must be dealt with before shipment is undertaken.

Some knowledge of the appropriate languages is, to say the least, desirable, however elementary it may be. A complete inability to communicate can make difficulties which otherwise would not have existed.

Finally, all disposable containers should be burnt after they have been emptied. Tanks should be thoroughly disinfected both inside and out, not forgetting the bed and sides of the truck, and the tyres.

11 Markets and opportunities

It is perhaps stating the obvious to say that the profitability
of a fish farm depends on its ability to produce goods that
will satisfy the market to which the farmer has access, at a
price which allows him a reasonable profit on his investment.
Market demands vary widely in different countries, as do
the costs of production and the prices obtainable, so before
setting up a farm a thorough research programme should be
carried out, including possibilities offered by the export
market, as well as local markets.

Hatchery products   Both brown and rainbow trout are sold for the table market
and for the purpose of re-stocking angling waters whose
natural stocks are depleted by over-fishing. Hatcheries
supply eggs, month-old fry and fingerlings to the trade and
are usually, though not always, associated with a fish farm,
where the products are taken through to market size. Some
large hatcheries, as well as selling their own products, act as
distribution centres, buying eggs from numerous sources
and selling them off again immediately, or at a later stage
of development. Establishments such as these provide a
market for small operators who prefer not to become
involved with extensive sale and distribution problems.

Where a hatchery is concerned with production of its
own eggs, it is necessary to maintain a brood stock. Mature

159

males are not usually kept on after stripping but, when they have recovered, are generally sold to the catering trade either live, fresh (iced), frozen or smoked; or they may be placed in stew ponds to recover and then used for re-stocking. The same applies to hen fish, though some operators keep them for perhaps another year's stripping. However, the egg yield may not be as good in their second year of maturity and it is more usual to build up an annually maturing brood stock, disposing of them after the first stripping. A hatchery can be, in itself, a successful business and since transport of eggs is possible by air over long distances, a profitable export trade can be established, particularly if a reputation is attained for high grade eggs delivered in the right quantities at the right time, and at the right price. As fish farms throughout the world become more numerous, there is an increasing trade in out-of-season eggs from one hemisphere to the other.

Re-stocking   Farming purely and simply for the purpose of re-stocking angling waters is profitable for the commercial operator only if he can deliver to an area where the demand for sport fisheries is sufficiently large to warrant specialization. On the smallest scale, unless the farm is regarded only as a means of providing an ancillary income it is not economic to produce less than about 12 tonnes per year. That means there must be a minimum requirement for, let us say, 80,000 fingerlings each of 150 gms for growing on, or 20,000 larger fish each of 0·6 kg. While sales may be made to angling clubs, put-and-take fisheries and riparian owners, large numbers of fish are not necessarily ordered in each individual case, so it is essential to establish and maintain a considerable number of outlets if profitability is to be continued.

Orders for larger numbers of fish may come from owners of large stretches of water such as extensive lakes or reservoirs deriving a part or all of their income from rod letting. However, land-owners operating stretches of water of this size very often have their own fish farms, and the same applies to local or state authorities, who are frequently the owners of this type of property. They often prefer to set up their own hatchery and on-growing facilities in order to keep down costs and at the same time maintain their stocks with fish whose health status they know. Nevertheless, if contracts – preferably long-term – can be negotiated for the supply of fish to interests such as these, a useful business can be established.

Re-stocking demand for rivers may be confined to brown trout in some areas, but rainbows are increasingly in demand, though here again management of the waters may be the responsibility of local authorities who prefer to use their own resources. However, there may be a call for larger fish later in the season if angling stocks have, for one reason or another, become depleted.

Trout destined for re-stocking are generally brought on to catchable size at a lower stocking density than those for the table market, since anglers are much concerned about the appearance of the fish they land, and there is consequently a demand for well-proportioned and anatomically perfect fish of good colour. Rearing on a highly intensive basis may result in some slight deformities as well as ragged fins and tails, and while this is often not particularly important in the case of those sold processed for the table, semi-intensive rearing is preferable in the case of those destined for sport fisheries.

Probably the majority of fish farmers cater principally for the table trade, but supply for re-stocking purposes if sufficiently large orders are placed with them in good time, or if they have stocks on hand due to cancelled orders, or for some other reason.

It is as well, however, to be informed on possible state subsidies or grants. Depending on the circumstances, they may be restricted to farms concerned with food production, and records of sales for re-stocking could invalidate claims. In other cases, of course, the opposite policy may hold good.

Table trade The demand for table trout falls principally into two categories: portion-sized fish of about 175-250 gms, and larger fish of up to roughly 1·15 kg for family consumption or the catering trade. The sizes demanded differ from place to place, according to the consumer's idea of what constitutes a portion. These products are usually sold frozen, often in packets of two, larger trout being sold singly.

Smoked trout of the same sizes are also popular in a number of countries.

The majority of small farms sell direct to processors or wholesalers, with whom it is important to build up a reputation for reliable delivery of fish of the right size. An ability to deliver fish of good quality and the right size on a regular basis, is of the utmost importance, particularly to processors, who will be selling frozen or smoked products under a trade name to retail outlets, and will not be keen to advertise goods they cannot supply.

Some farmers, however, prefer to install their own freezing and cold storage facilities as well as, in some cases, smokers, so that they can sell their products under their own name. The equipment is expensive, and a thorough analysis of the outlay, maintenance and labour costs and the returns should be carried out.

The shelf life of whole fish – fish 'in the round' – is short, only a day or two, and ungutted fish should not be frozen. If deliveries of this sort are made they should, therefore, not take too long in transit. Whether it is worthwhile installing a gutting machine is for individuals to decide in the light of the volume of trade, but if the fish are gutted on the premises the operation should be carried out as soon as possible after death. Whether the heads should be left on or not is, again, a matter for the purchaser to stipulate. After gutting, the remains of the kidney and blood vessels below the spine should be scraped out before icing. Gutted trout, iced, will keep in good condition for a week.

If the trout are frozen on the premises, they must be quick-frozen in a freezer and should then be wrapped in polythene, placed in containers and stored at $-10°C$. Under these conditions they should keep in first class condition for a month and two months in acceptable condition. At $-20°C$ the first class shelf life is five months and acceptable condition is 18 months.

One advantage of freezing on site is that fish can be stored and supplied to the market when the price is right, since the price on the wholesale market fluctuates according to the demand as well as the supply; glut conditions lower the price to the farmer. However, if the fish are sold iced, it is necessary to get rid of them at once, regardless of the state of the market.

Smoking, though not difficult, needs experience. Briefly, the smoke temperature is raised in two stages, being held at 30°C for half an hour and then 50°C for another half hour, before finally being brought up to 80°C where it is held for an hour or until the fish are thoroughly cooked.

Details of fish processing are available from

> Torry Research Station,
> 135 Abbey Road,
> Aberdeen,
> Scotland.

The relevant pamphlet is entitled: *Handling Rainbow Trout*.

Packaging regulations in some countries may demand tight envelopment of the fish in materials that exclude air. Frozen products, so long as they have not been contaminated, are not much affected by such regulations, but smoked fish could present a problem. If the wholesaler, retailer or purchaser keeps such fish in anaerobic conditions at a temperature that will allow development of *Clostridium botulinum*, this organism may develop and produce botulin toxin which, if ingested, is often fatal. Storage at −10°C or lower will prevent development of the bacterium.

Prior to slaughter fish should be starved for two or three days in order to empty the gut. As mentioned earlier, there is a demand for pink flesh, particularly with larger trout and food pellets containing canthaxanthin should be fed for three months before slaughter.

There is little call for brown trout for the table, principally because they grow more slowly than rainbows and are consequently less competitive in price.

Exports   If the export market is considered, another aspect that has to be taken into consideration is that of import taxes, which may be levied on some exporting countries and not on

163

others with which trade agreements have been made. These agreements may apply specifically to imports processed or packaged in certain ways. As a hypothetical example, country A may impose a 5 per cent tax on all imports of processed fish other than smoked, but tax smoked fish at a rate of 15 per cent except where special arrangements or agreements have been made. Wholesalers, export agents and large firms familiar with the market will be well acquainted with the situation, but the smaller operator attempting to increase his trade may price proposed exports of smoked fish at a rate which includes the usual 15 per cent import duty, whereas the country from which he is operating may, in fact, be liable only for 5 per cent. In such a case, his products will not be competitively priced, and he may lose orders he could have fulfilled had he made himself conversant with every detail of the regulations. The opposite can also happen – he may contract to supply smoked fish at a price costed on the basis of a 5 per cent duty, and find he has to pay 15 per cent.

Small farms While larger firms usually carry out their own processing and packaging as well as managing their own transport and handling home and export sales, the smaller farmer generally relies, for bulk sales, on deliveries of fresh fish to wholesalers or processors. However, if a sufficient number of farms can reach agreement, it is sometimes possible to set up a co-operative which can handle all the business of its members from start to finish, deliveries from individual farms being made to co-operative headquarters. Such a scheme cuts out intermediaries and can result in more competitively priced products.

The smaller farmer can often exploit local markets, particularly if his farm is situated reasonably close to a arge town or in a favourable locality such as a holiday area, where a good market is provided by the hotel and catering trade. Deliveries of fresh fish may be made to local outlets on a regular basis, and if there is a similar demand from further afield it is sometimes possible to arrange deliveries over quite a wide area by coming to an agreement with operators of refrigerated vans providing a regular delivery service of frozen foods to supermarkets or other large chains of stores.

Sales 'at the door' can increase the profits, and establishment of a shop or kiosk at the farm entrance may help.

Rod letting If the property is sufficiently large, rod letting can be profitable, particularly if it forms an additional income for a farm primarily concerned with production for other markets.

The best stocking density to aim at for an angling water is a matter for individual judgement. Anglers like some return for their money, but can become bored if fish are too easily caught. A fish population of something in the region of 120-150/hectare may be convenient as a starting figure, but should be re-assessed in the light of conversations with customers as well as observations made at the water-side. Understocking is obviously as undesirable as overstocking.

Put-and-take fisheries demand is, generally speaking, for fry or fingerlings for growing on.

Brown and rainbow trout are usually purchased in spring or autumn at 250-300 gms and intensively fed in stew ponds or floating cages until they have reached catchable size. While some anglers will be satisfied with catches of individual fish weighing something in the region of 0·5 kg, many will prefer larger specimens of 1 kg or more. Landing one or two big fish gives more pleasure than hooking a number of smaller ones.

Larger rainbows of 5-10 kg may attract a different type of customer prepared to pay more for his hobby, and fewer rods may be let at higher prices. Many anglers prefer to fish with a friend or in peaceful solitude, so that a large, irregularly shaped pond or a series of interconnected ponds affording some degree of privacy may be desirable. Car parking facilities are usually necessary, and possibly storage for tackle and clothing. Depending on the locality, the type of customer, and his ability and readiness to pay for his leisure activities, changing rooms, showers and other amenities may be considered. On a larger scale, a clubhouse and bar can provide an additional source of income, though they need staffing.

165

A strict account should be kept of the number of fish put into the ponds and the number taken out, so that under or overstocking is avoided, and as is the case with all fishery interests, an eye should be kept on the condition of the fish. Nothing destroys the reputation of fisheries of this type so quickly as badly fungussed or ulcerated fish being taken out by those who have paid – sometimes quite heavily – for their sport.

Other opportunities   There are other markets. Whether they are considered worthwhile or not depends not only on the type of farm and the financial resources available, but to a large extent on the individual preferences of the owner. Danish-type farms can bring some of the earth ponds into secondary – or even primary – use as a visitors' amenity in holiday resorts or beauty spots. Fish are usually bought as fingerlings and after growing to about 350 gms or even a little less are transferred to ponds open to the public. Visitors are charged for admission, and may also buy ready packaged bags of pelleted food with which they are permitted to feed the fish which, of course, they can also buy. This provides a self-financing form of feeding thus obviating, at any rate to some extent, one of the major items of expense on a fish farm. Part of the installation may be set aside for those who prefer to hire a rod and catch their own fish, and fresh or frozen trout can be sold at a shop or kiosk, which can also sell other suitable goods.

If the rest of the farm is used for more normal types of farming, it must be well separated from the public area by a fence, or the chances of contamination will be high. Although this type of fish amusement park may not appeal to all prospective fish farmers, it can be profitable, particularly if combined with sales of fresh or live fish to the local hotel and catering trade.

12 Legislation

Legislative aspects of aquaculture do not usually appeal to the fish farmer, who sometimes tends to regard them as an interference. Nevertheless, there are at least two useful reasons for introduction of control measures: the first is concerned with protecting responsible and competent farmers who do not want their water or stocks contaminated; and the second is in connection with issue of government or state-approved certificates of health which enable fish farmers to sell high grade stock to other countries whose authorities demand such certificates as a condition of import.

Controls on the introduction of exotic (ie non-indigenous) fish are often demanded by conservationists, on the grounds that newly-introduced species might displace the established fauna. Such arguments are often supported by sport fishermen, but cut across the demands of commercial aquaculturists wishing to breed improved stocks for the table market. The principal danger of imported exotics to the fish farmer is the possibility that they will bring with them diseases to which cultured stock may be susceptible. The consequence is that state controls over importation of fish from foreign countries generally meet with approval so long as they are not intolerably restrictive.

Certificates of health So far as international trade in trout is concerned, the principal demand from authorities is likely to be for certificates of health and, since they are more easily shipped than consignments of live fish and are less likely to carry infections, the first consideration is often given to egg certification. This is already a requirement of several states, and the number is likely to increase.

The type of certificate varies from country to country. Some ask merely for a statement that the shipment is 'to the best of my knowledge and belief free from disease'. Such assertions are worthless, though they may be a means of satisfying the import regulations of the country in order to ensure acceptance of shipments from known, desirable sources. On the other hand, if taken at its face value a certificate of this sort could be regarded as a contra-indication, since reputable suppliers are concerned with their good name and are not interested in producing ambiguous certificates.

Another phrase often seen on certificates is 'visual examination shows no sign of disease'. This is a little better, but not much. It depends on what has been seen: a quick look into a tank full of fish is not likely to be profitable, whereas the undetected presence of even one or two infected individuals may cause havoc after delivery. In any case, many diseases go through stages in which no visual signs are evident.

The problem of adequate certification of fish is difficult. It is obviously not feasible to examine every fish, so certificates have to be based on samples which indicate the health of the stock only on a statistical basis. Sampling procedures of this sort are useful when applied to a factory production line because they indicate the probable state of each product and those subsequently found to be faulty can be exchanged or repaired. But in health certification one or two faulty products (*ie* diseased fish) may very well result in the outbreak of an epidemic.

Sampling procedures at present adopted by more than one country provide a 95·0 per cent probability of detecting a 2·0 per cent incidence of infection in the population under test. On the face of it, this looks reasonable. But simple arithmetic shows that there is also a 5·0 per cent chance of failure to detect a 2·0 per cent incidence, and increasing probabilities of failure to discover incidence of less than 2·0 per cent.

Putting it in plainer terms, a health certificate acceptable in a number of countries possessing government laboratories with sophisticated analytical facilities, could allow import of 2,000 infected eggs in every 100,000 brought in; or a similar number of live fish, if live fish imports are permitted. Even improved sampling techniques are likely to permit import of 100 infected individuals in every 100,000 – and 100 diseased fish on a farm can do much damage.

Certificates of health, therefore, whatever their origin, should always be treated with caution. The best of them mean only that samples have been tested by laboratory procedures which, though scientifically reliable, cannot handle the practicalities of the situation.

There are numerous other possibilities: no official procedures can deal with the exporter who, holding a valid certificate for his brood stock, is unable to produce a sufficient number of eggs or fish to fulfill his orders and therefore slips the products of another farm into his shipment. If a single one of the fish he has bought in to make up the numbers is infected, the fish stocks on the recipient's farm are likely to pick up the disease, and no subsequent litigation can undo the damage. There is not, and never will be, any adequate substitute for buying good, clean, healthy stock from a reputable and reliable source which the purchaser himself knows well.

Local or national regulations Local or national regulations in connection with such matters as abstraction of water, discharge of effluents, construction of fish ladders and other similar activities are not always communicated as a matter of course to prospective fish farmers or to those purchasing an already existing property. It is wise, therefore, when setting up a fish farm, however small, to take legal advice from a lawyer conversant with both national and local fisheries legislation.

Fish farming in those countries in which there is little or

169

no controlling legislation, or where that which exists is not enforced is, in some ways, a simple and uncomplicated venture. So long as the farm is isolated or forms part of a village community, with ample supplies of water of the correct quality emanating from an uncontaminated source, all is well. If the trade is internal or is carried on with other states which, similarly, have few controls, the fish farmer has merely to look after his own interests. It is when other trading ventures impinge on the fishery that trouble can arise from contamination of the water by industrial or agricultural effluents or those from housing developments or, again, by dissemination of disease from uncontrolled and incompetently managed fish farms. As aquaculture and other industries develop, this type of situation can worsen until it is the fish farmer himself who may begin to plead for a greater degree of legislative control.

Glossary

Absorption	The passage of nutrients from the digestive tract into the blood stream.
Acclimatization	The process of accustoming fresh water fish to a salt water environment.
Alevins	Yolk sac fry. Very young fry which have not yet fully absorbed their yolk sacs.
Amino-acids	The structural units from which proteins are built.
Asphyxia	Suffocation. Deprivation of air or oxygen.
Broodstock	Sexually mature males or females kept for the purpose of producing fertilized eggs. Younger fish destined to be used for this purpose.
Buccal cavity	Mouth.
Buffering	A chemical reaction that helps to prevent changes in the acidity or alkalinity of a fluid.
Capillaries	Very small blood vessels which come into intimate contact with the cells of the body, taking oxygen and nutrients to them and carrying away excretory products and carbon dioxide.
Carbohydrates	Complex chemicals made up of linked sugar molecules.
Caudal	To do with the tail, or the posterior end of the fish.
Chemotherapy	Treatment of diseases by administration of drugs which have a damaging effect on the metabolism of microbes.
Chromosomes	Strings of genes situated in the cell nucleus.
Connective tissue	A type of tissue binding one organ to another.

Dermis	The lower layer of the skin (see epidermis).
Digestion	Enzymic breakdown of complex food substances such as proteins or carbohydrates into simpler substances which can be absorbed.
Dorsal	The side of the fish which is uppermost when it is swimming normally.
Effluent	Outflow. Point at which water is discharged from a fish farm. Used water flowing out of a farm.
Embryo	Developing fish within the egg.
Enzyme	An organic catalyst which accelerates the rate of a chemical reaction.
Epidermis	The outer layer of the skin, situated superficially to the dermis (*qv*).
Epithelium	A thin sheet of cells, often forming the boundary layer of an organ.
Equinox	Time when day and night are of equal length. Spring tides at the equinoxes (about 21 March and 22 September) are often higher and lower than usual, and storms often occur.
Extensive culture	Culture of fish in uncrowded conditions.
Eyed eggs	Eggs in which two black spots, which are the developing eyes of the embryo, can easily be seen.
Fats	Complex food substances made up of fatty acids and glycerol. Often used as a food reserve in the bodies of animals, and also function as insulating material.
Fatty acids	Chemicals which combine with glycerol to form fats. They consist of chains of carbon atoms linked with hydrogen, and terminate in a group with acidic properties.
Filtration	A procedure for separating particles of different sizes, analogous to sieving.
Fingerling	Term usually applied to trout of about 50-150 gms in weight, or 16·5-20 cms fork length.
First feeding fry	Fry which have absorbed their yolk sacs and are ready to begin feeding.
Flagellum	A very thin protoplasmic projection from a cell, capable of a whip-like or rotary movement which can propel the cell through a fluid medium.
Fork length	Length between tip of snout and centre of the tail fork.
Fry	Hatchlings weighing up to 50 gms or having a fork length less than 16·5 cms.
Gene	That part of the chromosome concerned with the

	development of hereditary characters.
Glycerol	A sweet, sticky liquid which combines with fatty acids to form fats.
Grading	A means of separating larger fish from smaller by passing them through a type of filter, or sieve, made of bars. Those fish fatter than the apertures between the bars are retained, while thinner fish pass through.
Growers	Fish past the fingerling stage, growing up to marketable size.
Haem(-al)	To do with blood.
Intensive culture	Technique for growing fish to marketable size in very crowded conditions.
Invertebrate	Without a backbone.
Iodophore	A complex chemical compound which, on exposure to water, releases iodine. Can be used in appropriate concentrations for disinfecting eggs or equipment, but is highly toxic to fish.
Ion	A charged particle. Atomic nuclei possess a positive charge which is normally neutralized by the negatively charged electrons which form a cloud round it. If an electron is lost, there will be a residual positive charge and the resulting ion will be a positively charged ion. If an electron is gained, the resulting ion will be negatively charged.
Lamella	A thin, leaf-like structure.
Lateral	To do with the side of the body, or sideways movement.
Lumen	The interior of a tubular structure.
Lymphatic	A thin-walled open ended vessel into which the tissue fluids drain. Lymphatics open finally into a vein, which returns the fluids to the blood.
Metabolism	The many chemical and physiological processes that go on in a living organism.
Metabolites	Substances resulting from metabolic processes. The word usually refers to waste substances, some of which may be toxic.
Microbe	A word commonly used to denote a very small disease-causing organism.
Micro-organism	A very small organism, usually visible only with the aid of a microscope.
Micropyle	An aperture in the outer covering of an unfertilized egg through which the sperm passes in order to fuse with the

	egg nucleus and so fertilize the egg.
Monk	A structure built into the banking of a pond, which can be set to regulate the depth of water. It contains a screen which allows water to flow through, but prevents the escape of fish.
Neural	To do with nerves.
Nucleus	That part of the cell containing the chromosomes as well as other components concerned with the control of the cell and its functions.
Oil	A fat which remains liquid at low temperatures.
Olfactory	To do with the sense of smell.
Organ	An anatomically and physiologically discrete body structure composed of a number of tissues which function in co-ordination with one another.
Organic	Derived from living matter. Containing carbon.
Organism	An animal or plant.
Osmosis	If a fluid containing a high salt concentration is separated from one containing a lower concentration of salt by a membrane that allows the passage through it of the fluid but not of the dissolved salt, the fluid will tend to pass through the membrane in such a way that the salt concentrations on both sides of the membrane are equalized. The passage of water through a membrane (a so-called semi-permeable membrane, because it permits passage of some substances but not others) in this way is known as osmosis.
Osmotic shock	The physiological disturbance to the tissues of a fish caused by the uncontrolled passage (into or out of them) of water as a result of osmotic movement of the water.
Ossification	Replacement of a tissue (usually cartilage) by bone.
Pathogen	A medical term for a parasite which causes a disease in its host.
pH	A measure of the concentration of hydrogen ions in water: thus a measure of the acidity or alkalinity of the water. pH 7·0 is neutral, with an equal number of H^+ and OH^- ions (HOH – or H_2O – being the chemical formula for water). An increase of H^+ ions increases the acidity and the pH falls to a lower level than 7·0. pH 1·0 is very acid. A decrease in the number of H^+ ions brings about a concomitant increase in the number of OH^- ions, the pH reaches a greater level than 7·0 and the fluid becomes more alkaline.

Photosynthesis	The process by which green plants absorb sunlight, using it as a source of energy. Plants respire by day and by night, but photosynthesize only in daylight. During the day, more oxygen is produced by photosynthesis than is used in respiration, but during the night no photosynthesis takes place though respiration continues, and uses up oxygen in the water. During hot weather, when the oxygen content of water is low, the respiratory activity of plants in darkness may reduce the oxygen content of the water to a level too low for trout, which are consequently asphyxiated and found dead in the morning.
Plasma	The fluid in which blood cells float.
Polysaccharides	Another name for carbohydrates.
Portion size	Fish of a size suitable for consumption by one person. The size varies in different markets, but is often applied to fish of 150-250 gms or a fork length of about 24-30 cms.
Potable water	Drinking water. Water treated in such a way as to render it suitable for consumption.
Protein	A complex chemical formed of intertwined chains of amino-acids.
Protoplasm	A jelly-like substance forming the main part of the body of a cell. That part of the cell other than the nucleus. Protoplasm is extremely complex in structure and is, in reality, the old name for those cellular components about which little was known in earlier years. The term is still retained as being useful to describe the generality of those cell structures situated outside the nucleus.
Protozoa	Single-celled animals or plants often with a complex internal organization analagous, on a microscopic scale to the internal organization of some higher groups. Some possess locomotor as well as sensory organs. Usually free-living in fluids, but some are parasitic.
Put-and-take fishery	Ponds or lakes provided for angling. They are re-stocked when necessary with cultivated fish.
Re-cycling	Re-use of water. Water is returned to the same or a different location to be used again.
Sac	A membranous bag.
Saturated	Holding as much it can. Saturated water at 4°C holds 12·88 ppm oxygen, while that at 20°C holds only 9·00 ppm oxygen. Both waters are fully saturated at those temperatures.

Semi-intensive culture	Culture of fish under more crowded conditions than would be usual in nature, but not as crowded as in intensive culture.
Semi-permeable	Permitting passage of some substances but not others.
Sinus	A chamber.
Sluice	A water gate. A sliding gate by means of which the level of water in a pond can be adjusted, or the flow of water regulated.
Specific gravity	The weight of a fish compared to the weight of the same volume of water.
Sperm	Spermatozoon. The male sex cell. Male gamete.
Sphincter	A circular muscular valve, guarding an orifice.
Splashboard	A plank or board – or any other solid object – placed below a water intake, so that the inflowing water falls on it and splashes. Used as a simple aerating mechanism.
Stocking density	Number of fish per unit volume of water. Usually measured as the number per cubic metre, or weight per cubic metre.
Swim-up fry	Fry which have just absorbed their yolk sacs and are ready to take food.
Temperate	Cool, moderate.
Tissue fluids	Those fluids which, having drained through the walls of capillary blood vessels, bathe the surfaces of cells, tissues and organs.
Tonne	Metric ton. 1,000 kg. 0.9842 imp. tons.
Toxic	Poisonous.
Toxicity	Capacity to cause damage by poisoning. A measure of this capacity.
Unicellular	Consisting of only one cell.
Ventral	The underside of a fish as it swims normally.
Venturi	An orifice in a pipe which, because of the vacuum created in it by the swift passage of fluid through the pipe, sucks air into the pipe.
Vertebrate	Possessing a backbone.
Vitamin	A chemical forming an essential part of the diet. Vitamins usually play a part in intra-cellular metabolism.
Yolk-sac	The membranous bag which contains the yolk within an egg. The bag remains connected to the intestine of the hatchling, supplying it with food until it develops the capability of swimming.
Yolk-sac fry	Very young fry with the yolk sac still attached. Another name for Alevins.

Appendix

Biology

B. Curtis. *The life story of the fish.* Dover publications Inc., New York, USA. 1949.

W. E. Frost. *A survey of rainbow trout* Salmo gairdneri *in Great Britain and Ireland.* Freshwater Biological Association, The Ferry House, Far Sawrey, Ambleside, Cumbria, England. 1974

W. E. Frost & M. E. Brown. *The trout.* Collins, London. 1967.

H. L. Helmprecht & L. T. Friedman. *Basic chemistry for the life sciences.* McGraw-Hill, London, England. 1977.

T. T. Macan & E. B. Worthington. *Life in lakes and rivers.* Collins, London, England. 1951.

N. B. Marshall. *The life of fishes.* Weidenfeld & Nicolson, London, England. 1965.

L. Peart. *Trout and trout waters.* Allen & Unwin, London, England. 1956.

Anatomy & Physiology

M. E. Brown. *The physiology of fishes.* Academic Press, London, England. 1960.

W. S. Hoar & D. J. Randall. *Fish physiology.* Academic Press, London, England. 1969.

Pathology

R. J. Roberts (Editor). *Fish pathology.* Baillière Tindall, London, England. 1978.

R. J. Roberts & C. J. Shepherd. *Handbook of trout and salmon diseases.* Fishing News Books Ltd, Farnham, England. 1974

Aquaculture	J. E. Bardach, J. H. Ryther, W. O. McLarney. *Aquaculture*. John Wiley & Sons, Inc, New York, USA. 1972
	H. S. Davis. *Culture and diseases of game fishes.* University of California Press, Berkeley, California, USA. 1965.
	D. J. Edwards. *Salmon and Trout Farming in Norway.* Fishing News Books Ltd, Farnham, England. 1978.
	M. Huet. *Textbook of fish culture.* Fishing News Books Ltd, Farnham, England.
	E. Leitritz & R. C. Lewis. *Trout and salmon culture (Hatchery methods).* State of California, Department of Fish & Game. 1976.
	S. D. Sedgwick. *Trout farming handbook.* Seeley Service & Co, London, England. 1976.
Water quality	E. Windle Taylor. *The examination of water and water supplies.* J. & A. Churchill Ltd, London, England. 1958.
Food hygiene	Report. *Fish and shellfish hygiene.* Food & Agricultural Organization of the United Nations. Rome. 1974.
Journals	*Aquaculture.* Elsevier Scientific Publishing Co, Associated Scientific Publishers, Journal Division, PO Box 211, 1000 AE Amsterdam, The Netherlands.
	Fish Farmer. 1 Throwley Way, Sutton, Surrey, England.
	Fish Farming International. 110 Fleet Street, London EC4A 2JL, England.
	Journal of Fish Diseases. Blackwell Scientific Publications, Osney Mead, Oxford OX2 0EL, England.
	The Progressive Fish Culturist. United States Department of the Interior, Fish & Wildlife Service, Aylesworth Hall, Colorado State University, Fort Collins, Colorado 80523, USA.

Index

Abdominal cavity, 95
Absorption, 49
Access, 38, 150
Acclimatization, 68-71
Acetone, 93
Acidity, 9, 10
Acoustico-lateralis system, 116, 119, 125, 126-127
Aeration, 8, 9, 13, 18, 36, 39, 40, 56, 58-59, 71, 78, 90, 92, 140, 153, 154
Aeromonas, 142, 148
Air bladder, see swim bladder
Alarms, 73, 74, 77
Alcohol, 93
Alevins, 11, 78, 81, 106, 107, 110, 130
Algae, 12, 39
Alkalinity, 11
Altitude, 12
Amino acid, 3, 49
Ammonia, 36, 58, 122, 155
Anaesthetic, 93
Analysis, see water
Antibiotic, 136, 149
Antibody, 144-149
Antigen, 144-149
Argulus, 133
Asphyxia, 11, 13
Automatic egg sorter, 110-111
Back channel, 23, 36
Back-flushing, 37, 38
Bacteria, 36, 116, 133-136, 142, see also under individual headings
Balance, 119
Banks, 23
Basket, 78, 80, 105, 107, 109, 151
Beam balance, 48
Behaviour, 2, 48, 137
Benzocaine, 93
Biological filter, 36
Blood, 124, 127-128, 142, 147
BOD, 10
Borehole, 11, 16, 75, 81
Bottle, 80, 83, 105, 106
Breeding, 92, 104
Broodstock, 11, 15, 16, 60, 61, 68, 75, 90-100, 159, 169
Buffer, 10, 62
By-pass, 8, 36, 38, 83
Cages, 39, 58, 61, 63, 64-68, 69, 72, 73, 92
Calcium bicarbonate, 10
Calcium carbonate, 10

Cannibalism, 44
Canthaxanthin, 51, 163
Capital, 4, 61
Carbohydrate, 49, 50
Carbon dioxide, 10, 93
Carotenoid, 116
Carrier, 137, 138, 142, 148
Cascade, 59
Catering trade, 61, 161, 164, 166
Cell, 115, 134
Central nervous system, 117, 120, 124-126
Chemotherapy, 134, 136-137, 149
Chlorbutanol, 93
Chlorine, 9, 10, 15, 44
Chromatophore, 116
Circulation, see water
Classification, 113-115
Cleaning, 38, 83, 110
Climate, 93, 157
Cold storage, 76, 162
Comparator, 9
Compressor, 59
Condition factor, 52
Contamination, see pollution
Conversion rate, 51, 55, 109
Co-operative, 164
Corrosion, 65
Costiasis, 140
Course, see water
Crowding, 45, 46, 47, 92, 144
Culture, see production
Culture facilities, 17-24
Current, 65
Customs, 151, 158
Dam, 17
Damage, 42
Danish ponds, 15, 17-24, 36, 109, 166
Day length, 12, 49, 131
Debris, see detritus
Delivery, 42, 48, 69, 150, 156, 164
Depth, see water
Dermis, 116
Detritus, 8, 27, 37, 68, 73, 78, 81, 82, 107
Development, see growth
Diesel, 16
Diet, 3, 4, 49-52, 72, 90, 132
Diffuser, 152
Digestion, 49, 121-122
Discharge, see effluent
Disease, 2, 3, 11, 15, 36, 41, 42, 43-44, 51, 55, 58, 66, 75, 104, 131, 132-149, 167, 168, 169
Disinfection, 15, 43, 44, 94, 106, 107, 158
Distribution, see water

179

**Other books published by Fishing News Books
Limited, Farnham, Surrey, England.**

Free catalogue available on request

Advances in aquaculture
Aquaculture practices in Taiwan
Better angling with simple science
British freshwater fishes
Commercial fishing methods
Control of fish quality
Culture of bivalve molluscs
The edible crab and its fishery in British waters
Eel capture, culture, processing and marketing
Eel culture
European inland water fish: a multilingual catalogue
FAO catalogue of fishing gear designs
FAO catalogue of small scale fishing gear
FAO investigates ferro-cement fishing craft
Farming the edge of the sea
Fish and shellfish farming in coastal waters
Fish catching methods of the world
Fish inspection and quality control
Fisheries of Australia
Fisheries oceanography
Fishery products
Fishing boats and their equipment
Fishing boats of the world 1
Fishing boats of the world 2
Fishing boats of the world 3
The fishing cadet's handbook
Fishing ports and markets
Fishing with electricity
Fishing with light
Freezing and irradiation of fish

Handbook of trout and salmon diseases
Handy medical guide for seafarers
How to make and set nets
Inshore fishing: its skills, risks, rewards
International regulation of marine fisheries: a study of
regional fisheries organizations
The lemon sole
A living from lobsters
Marine pollution and sea life
The marketing of shellfish
Mechanization of small fishing craft
Mending of fishing nets
Modern deep sea trawling gear
Modern fishing gear of the world 1
Modern fishing gear of the world 2
Modern fishing gear of the world 3
More Scottish fishing craft and their work
Multilingual dictionary of fish and fish products
Navigation primer for fishermen
Netting materials for fishing gear
Pair trawling and pair seining – the technology of two boat
fishing
Pelagic and semi-pelagic trawling gear
Planning of aquaculture development – an introductory guide
Power transmission and automation for ships and
submersibles
Refrigeration on fishing vessels
Salmon and trout farming in Norway
Salmon fisheries of Scotland
Seafood fishing for amateur and professional
The seine net: its origin, evolution and use
Ships' gear '66
Sonar in fisheries: a forward look
Stability and trim of fishing vessels
The stern trawler
Testing the freshness of frozen fish
Textbook of fish culture: breeding and cultivation of fish
Training fishermen at sea
Trawlermen's handbook
Tuna: distribution and migration